ALLEN BREED SERIES

CW00329593

The Appaloosa

The late Dorian Williams, president of the British Appaloosa Society, presenting the cup to Ken de Rivaz and Klaus, who was National Champion Stallion ten times.

ALLEN BREED SERIES

The Appaloosa

Ann Hyland

J. A. Allen
London

British Library Cataloguing in Publication Data
Hyland, Ann
  The Appaloosa.
  1. Appaloosa horses
  I. Title
  636.13

ISBN 0–85131–506–2

Published in Great Britain in 1990 by
J. A. Allen & Company Limited
1 Lower Grosvenor Place
London SW1W 0EL

Series editor Elizabeth O'Beirne-Ranelagh
Book production Bill Ireson
Printed in Great Britain by The Bath Press, Avon

To George
thank you for caring for Nizzolan, Granicus and Katchina
whilst I muster material

Contents

Front cover: The Leopard. Detail from a painting by John Ferneley, Snr., the early-nineteenth-century British sporting artist.

Endpapers: Tibertich Appaloosas in Argyll, Scotland.

Acknowledgements

When writing any book with an element of equine history, especially one about current and recent horses, the help of many people goes towards fleshing the bones and making the horses come alive.

As this is largely a book about British Appaloosas I am indebted to Michael Howkins of the British Appaloosa Society and to the Society in general for making all Society records available to me and for permission to publish the certificate appearing on p. 50. The Australian and Canadian Appaloosa Societies also kindly furnished me with up-to-date rule books and literature so that comparisons could be made in systems of registration and in performance fields. I would also like to thank the many Appaloosa owners who answered detailed questions about their horses, afforded me interviews, and in many cases furnished me with a good selection of photographs of their horses. In particular I should like to mention Nigel and Lucia Boase of Ardfern who supplied prompter than prompt answers, photographs and some thought-provoking assessments. The photographs they provided are those on pp. 31, 44–5, 65, 106, 132 and the endpapers of the book. Especial thanks go to the de Rivaz family for their hospitality, information, and a wealth of pictures of our early British Appaloosas taken by Oliver Brazier, who in turn agreed to their request that I use them as a record of the Society's early days. Between them they provided the photographs on pp. iv, 1, 23, 29, 31, 33, 35, 36, 41–3, 69, 70, 77, 88, 94, 96 and 97. I would not have been able to flesh out the index with the registration numbers of British horses without the help of Marilyn Hollanders, who also sent me the photographs on pp. 33 and 78 (the latter taken by Frazer Clement); and Paul and Maj-Britt Carter enabled me to write a much fuller account of the Danish Knabstrup than usually appears when it is mentioned in a British publication. The photograph on p. 26 is theirs.

From the other side of the Atlantic Sharon Saare kept me supplied with a continuous flow of information, the current American rule book, notes on performance horses, and a selection of superb photographs (on pp. 20, 99, 124, 127, 128, 133, 134, 135 and 136) from her own collection and also from others, with their permission to publish, especially those by June Fallow (p. 99), Pamela Davis (p. 124), Charles Barrieau (p. 127) and George Axt (p. 135).

Thanks are due to all the others who provided photographs: Jim Dobson (pp. 59, 119), Bob and Ellie Gale (p. 72), John and Brenda George (p. 113), John Luckett (pp. 57, 85), Brugs Nichols (pp. 77, 122), Jim and Joyce Nutland (pp. 93, 115) and John and Joan Sillitoe (pp. 101, 104, 139); and to the people and institutions who have granted permission for publication: the John Rylands University Library of Manchester (pp. 6, 7), the Dean and Chapter of Hereford (p. 9), Harvey Miller Publishers (pp. 11, 12), the Marquess of Hertford (p. 13) and EMAP (p. 109). The photographs on pp. 46, 47, 54, 74, 102, 107, 110, 111, 116, 119 and 120 are my own. Wyn Hughes found the photograph for the cover illustration, which is reproduced by courtesy of Sotheby's.

Finally, thanks to the Appaloosa itself. I have added to my knowledge since writing this book, and maybe one of the most significant findings is that as a breed the Appaloosa ranks amongst the oldest, if not the oldest, in recorded history.

ANN HYLAND

1 Introduction

In the small compass of this book I have tried to convey to Appaloosa lovers a different overview of a breed which is once more enjoying a wide geographical spread after many decades of being considered, erroneously, a purely American breed. The only thing purely American is the Indian name 'Appaloosa'.

Much of the history of the breed and its earlier origins have been covered before, but I have had the good fortune to find additional references in literature rather than art. I would also suggest that the Spanish influence existed far earlier than the dates usually ascribed to the main thread of the breed's history; this too is found in literature, but in the form of a military record.

The core of the book deals largely with the current state of the Appaloosa horse in Britain. This is balanced by a look at the breed's transatlantic kin, with special credit

Appaloosa mare and foal: the Rivaz Stud's Asterisk with foal by Pendean Bobby.

to Claude Thompson and Dr Francis Haines, without whom there would be no Appaloosa breed registry in the USA or subsequently in the UK. The Australian Appaloosa Association and the Appaloosa Horse Club of Canada are also featured.

As with most breeds of horse there is always room for differences of opinion about what is the best of breed and how that perfect animal is produced within the legitimate breed registration rules.

The final section contains a selection of horses and Appaloosa afficionados who have made their mark in the early years of the modern Appaloosa's British chapter. A few from America are introduced to British readers, mainly from the sphere of endurance riding, but also through the generous help of my friend Sharon Saare, who is always ready with a fund of information. This section is not comprehensive. It would need a far larger volume to cover the contribution all British breeders have made to the Appaloosa horse. American Appaloosas of note would require several volumes to do them justice.

For space reasons too I have made no attempt to go deeply into extended pedigrees of the main foundation horses. Neither have I attempted any analysis of the thorny problem of Appaloosa genetics, particularly as this is open to much speculation. Both these areas would require a comprehensive treatment outside the scope of this work.

I have, however, done my level best to pay tribute to this spectacular Everyman's Horse and to the people in whose care his future in Britain lies.

2 History of the Appaloosa horse

The Appaloosa, with his melange of brightly hued coat patterns, is undoubtedly one of the most distinctive of the world's breeds. In the past fifty years the Appaloosa has come from near obscurity in America to ranking third in numerical standing amongst the registered breeds of the USA, and is also rapidly gaining ground in many other countries. Much has been accomplished since 1938 when the combined efforts of horseman Claude Thompson and historian Dr Francis Haines resulted in the official founding of the Appaloosa Horse Club, Inc. (ApHC). This major step in forming an association to preserve and promote the Appaloosa breed of horse, though important in setting up an official registry, was only one more milestone for a type of horse that goes back to the dawn of recorded history.

For the moment I use the word 'type' rather than 'breed' intentionally, because in the ancient world when man first started using horses, at first as food, then as a means of transport, and finally as the vital component in armies bent on long-range conquest, the term 'breed' as we understand it, with the concern over retaining breed integrity and purity of blood, did not exist. That was to come later, as literary records from Persia, Greece and Rome show.

Early depictions of spotted horses

In the Upper Paleolithic age, some 20,000 years ago, the horse was a meat animal along with other herbivores, and it is from this era that the first depiction of spotted horses comes. The cave paintings of the Lascaux area in France include several tableaux showing horses, and quite a number have spotted hides. Three in particular are worth mentioning: two horses in the main Grotte du Pech-Merle at Cabrerets, in a panel measuring 13 feet, and another single horse in another section of the same cave grouping. In the Grotte de la Justice, Boutigny-sur-Essone, in the *département* of Essone in the Ile de France, another spotted horse is shown similar to those in the Pech-Merle system. They all show leopard markings. (For an explanation of Appaloosa markings see pp. 40–5.)

In the Mediterranean world scenes of spotted horses crop up often enough in various art forms from different locations to suggest that around the fourteenth century BC the spotted horse was fairly widespread, though the indications should be treated with caution. A crude terra cotta statuette of chariot and charioteer with horses, which have definite spots painted in the shoulders, dates to 1300 BC, and a tomb in Enkomi, Cyprus, yielded a Cypro-Mycenaen krater (mixing vessel for wine) which shows very definite snowflake markings (white spots on a darker ground). A vase with a related scene but a more stylized depiction of the spots on the horse came from Mycenae itself, and also dates from the fourteenth century BC. From an historical point of view this could mean that the pottery all stemmed from one area, or since there are distinct differences in the workmanship, it may have been made in different locales.

In the ancient world movement of horses was conducted by sea by *hippago* (horse transport), and there was definitely a movement of horses for racing purposes by Homer's day (eighth century BC). He records teams from Thrace (Greece/ Bulgaria), Achaean Pthia, Tros (Truva in modern Turkey), and Pylia. By Sophocles' day (fifth century BC) they travelled even further. In the *Electra* he names the opponents of Orestes in the chariot race at Delphi, and whereas most of the teams came from one or other of the Greek provinces, two came from Libya.

Archaeologists, usually not much concerned with equestrian matters, have from time to time turned up artefacts that show spotted horses. One such is the sword scabbard from the Hallstatt site in Austria dating from the eighth century BC. Incised on the iron are definite spotting marks on three of the four horses, two of which have spotted rumps in addition to other areas such as belly, neck, and in one case chest. However, the legs are also banded in a way similar to the tiger or zebra banding often seen on dun horses. The riders' trousers are gartered, and one horse's tail is cross banded. The Celts evolved their own highly stylized art forms, so this representation should be used with caution. If the leg banding represents support wraps then the spots are indicative. If not, they could be artist's licence. Support wraps were well known to the Romans, as indicated by one of the excellent mosaics in the Sousse museum in Tunisia which shows four racing stallions so equipped. Roman mosaics recorded detail very accurately.

Further on in time, in the late second century AD, we find the poet Oppian writing his *Cynegetica*, a treatise on all forms of hunting, for the current Roman emperor, Caracalla. Much of Roman horse lore is couched in fable form behind which lies hard fact. Oppian describes an animal called the Orynx which is quite clearly an Appaloosa type of horse, but not understanding the genetic reasons for the colouring he explains it as the foal being branded with 'the flaming bronze' to acquire the spots. Branding of this sort would leave a different texture to the newly grown hair and alter its colour, provided that it did not destroy the follicles altogether, and one of the

Appaloosa traits is that the spots can be felt as well as seen. Many of Oppian's other descriptions, of different animals and birds as well as horses, concerning colour genetics are also in fable form.

It is often thought that the Spanish influence started about the time of the Conquistadores in the late fifteenth and early sixteenth centuries AD, with a limited amount of such influence dating back to mid-medieval times. However, it is worth investigating the Roman military records of the first century AD. In that century, around AD 70 during Vespasian's reign and some years either side of it as well, considerable numbers of cavalry units were raised in many Roman provinces. In Tarraconensis (northern Spain) a total of 8,250 cavalrymen with mounts and remounts was raised. Of interest is that these units were posted, among other places, to countries that we know had spotted horses at a later date, such as Britain, Noricum (Austria), Raetia (Switzerland), Germany and Dalmatia. This is not conclusive by any means but it does suggest that the spotted horse may have reached a wide European base well before the medieval Spanish exports. It is unlikely that the spots suddenly appeared from Spain in the later shipments.

The Romans by and large did not have colour preferences, except white for ceremonial duties with religious associations, so the colours would not have been recorded accurately for large contingents. However, the records of the XXth Palmyrene Cohort Equitata for the year AD 251, when they were stationed at Dura Europus on the Euphrates, does record colours for individual horses purchased. One is a four-year-old mare coloured 'frosty bay' – one of the less distinctive Appaloosa coat patterns, or a red roan?

In recorded history China has a varied selection of spotted horses shown in both art and statuary. Claims have been made that the first spotted Chinese horses descended from the horses brought from Ferghana in the late second century BC by the Emperor Wu Ti. He ordered a protracted campaign covering many years and costing thousands of human and animal lives in order to acquire superior stock to cross on to the inferior and small Chinese war horses. At that time the Huns were constantly harrying the Chinese, as they were to do later in the Christian era as Rome's influence waned. Whether any among the Ferghana horses did sport spots cannot be proved, but from that time on horses of Appaloosa colouring began to appear in Chinese art depicted as war horses, hunters and polo ponies. Many of these spotted horse statues come from the seventh century AD T'ang Dynasty, and appear frequently in succeeding dynasties. Two examples from the T'ang Dynasty are of sporting horses. One pottery horse is a light chestnut with a pale mane and tail, with irregular dark spots on body and legs. The horse is carrying a rider and a cheetah used for hunting. It was excavated in 1964 from the tomb of Princess Yung Fei T'ai at Ch'ien-Hsien near Sian and dates to AD 706. The other T'ang example is a copy of a wall painting from the tomb of Prince Chan Huai (Li Hsien), also from the site at Ch'ien-Hsien. The painting is of polo players and one horse shows leopard markings on neck and rump, and unlike many in Chinese paintings this horse has a refined head.

Another dynasty famous for popularizing the horse was the Yuan Dynasty. Its first ruler Kublai Khan and his successors naturally possessed the Mongols' love of horses. The Yuan Dynasty lasted from AD 1260 to 1368 and in that time Kublai Khan established himself in Peking and became a noted patron of painters. Foremost amongst these was Chao Meng-Fu, and the Yuan court style of painting returned to the vigorous manner of the T'ang painters with their predilection for equestrian art. Two noted painters who followed Chao Meng-Fu were Jen Jen-Fa and Kung K'au, who devoted themselves to painting horses. The Yuan style was also followed in the

The Persian hero Rustom with his horse Raksh as depicted by (*below*) the sixteenth-century Tabriz school and (*opposite page*) the seventeenth-century Isfahan school of art. Notice the white sclera around the eye and the striped hooves.

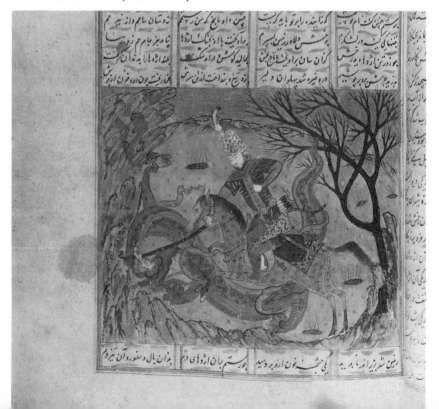

long-lived Ming Dynasty that followed the Yuan and ruled until 1644. Many equestrian paintings from the Ming era survive and among them spotted horses are frequent, mostly of the leopard variety.

Evidence for spotted horses also comes from Persia. Their great hero Rustom and his horse Raksh appear in legends dating to the second half of the first millennium BC. These passed, mostly verbally, until codified into the great Persian epic poem, the *Shahnama*, by the poet Firdausi in the tenth century AD. Firdausi tells of the meeting of Rustom with his steed Raksh. Raksh was running with his dam amongst a herd of spotted steeds, and Firdausi notes that he was a spotted bay. In the sixteenth and seventeenth centuries the schools of Isfahan, Tabriz and Shiraz all produced paintings of the Rustom legends and in all these Raksh is shown as a leopard spot. Other Persian miniatures of battle scenes show spotted horses of both leopard and blanket variety. As with all Persian paintings the horses are of a refined build, of Arabian type, but this is artistic convention as they also showed the Mongol hordes on similarly refined steeds, quite unlike the steppe animals the Mongol tumans

actually rode to battle, even allowing for the fact that much of the Mongol cavalry was supplemented with captured and tribute horses along their path of conquest.

The Spanish and European influence

Spanish church art of the eighth century AD had an early example of spotted horses in a manuscript now in the British Museum. The Four Horsemen of the Apocalypse are shown on their respective mounts, three of which are spotted, one markedly so with a very loud rust leopard patterning. Later European bestiaries and other manuscript illuminations frequently show examples of leopard markings. They are found from a wide geographic range. An early-thirteenth-century tapestry from Baldishol in Norway shows a mail-clad knight in armour identical to that depicted in the Bayeux Tapestry. His chestnut black-spot leopard wears a Norman type of war saddle. Armour and horse accoutrements did not change radically in the time span of just over a century that separates Senlac Hill in 1066 and the early thirteenth century, and this detail suggests the general accuracy of the tapestry. A French fifteenth-century manuscript depicting a tournament at St Anglevert in 1390 shows one combatant astride a red-spot, white base-colour leopard. Again the artist has been very careful to depict the armour and accoutrements of both horse and rider in accurate detail. The only anomaly is the inclusion of a tilt, which was in use when the manuscript was painted, but not when the tournament depicted took place.

A thirteenth-century example of the Appaloosa gives it possibly its earliest claim to being a universal horse, predating by 700 years its current worldwide spread. A strikingly marked leopard stallion strides away beyond Africa at the far edge of Hereford Cathedral's priceless treasure, the *Mappa Mundi* (*c.* 1280). Its claim to universality can be understood, as much art of the era was allegorical and meant for those who could not read.

All the countries noted above were known to have had trade links and/or war connections with Asia Minor for many centuries, and considering that the artistic details were representative of the ages in which they were painted, more than the era of the action, it suggests that the spotted horse was hardly a rarity in early and late medieval Europe. In fact the manuscripts and illustrations from the Norman to Plantagenet periods in Europe show so many examples of leopard-spotted horses that one is led to believe that Appaloosa patterns were as normal as any other coat colours; one particularly fine military example is seen charging across the prologue to Geoffrey of Monmouth's *History of the Kings of Britain* (*c.* 1136).

8

The bottom right-hand corner of the thirteenth-century *Mappa Mundi* depicting the little-known countries of Africa.

In literature too there is the occasional reference. The Middle High German poem 'Willehalm' by Sir Wolfram of Eschenbach, written in the 1220s, recounts the earlier tale of the Battle of Alischanz (Aliscans in French), which had originally appeared in written form in French thirty years earlier. The central theme and figure is William of Toulouse, cousin to Charlemagne, and his exploits leading up to the two battles of

9

Alischanz in the closing years of the eighth and first years of the ninth centuries (793 and 803). William, fighting for his own lands of Toulouse and later for Charlemagne, took the war into Spain against the Moslems. From the equestrian angle the poem is very interesting, giving details of armour and training, albeit of the era in which it was written, rather than the age it dealt with. The horse William originally rode was named Puzzat in 'Willehalm', and in the earlier French 'Aliscans' it was called Baucent or Bauchant, which translates as 'Whitespots'. Passilivrier was the mount of the Moslem Sinagun, King of Bailie, and Wolfram describes him as 'swift, dragon hued, spotted all over as it were with fiery sparks; and swifter than a deer'. Here we get a hint of spotted horses in different base coat colours but both of Appaloosa type – a snowflake and a red-spot leopard. The French horse could well have been imported from Spain as elsewhere William's brother Arnalt is described as riding a Castilian horse. The Moslems had of course been in Spain for centuries. Spain was continuing her long history of producing top-class horseflesh, and supplied war horses to much of the European chivalry throughout the medieval era.

Spanish influence continued to be felt in both the human and equestrian spheres throughout much of Europe. Spain ruled southern Italy from 1502 to 1707, and thus the Neapolitan stock was heavily infused with Spanish blood which then found its way into England, Germany and Austria, as well as other European countries. Holland felt the might of Spain and its inquisition and in 1519 the Netherlands came under Spanish rule. King Frederick II of Denmark founded his stud in 1562 using Spanish stock, while only a few years later in the Hapsburg Empire, the famous Lipizza breeding grounds passed to Archduke Charles, nephew of the Charles I of Castile who became Charles V of the Holy Roman Empire. Later the Spanish stud was expanded under Emperor Charles VI, who built the Winter Riding School at Vienna in 1732.

It is to this later age, when the day of the battle horse was over, and the era of haute école started to make an impact, that much of the pictorial evidence for Appaloosas dates. There is a rich source of material showing these animals, mostly leopard-spotted black on a white base colour. One of the best collections of paintings of the High School Horse are at Wilton House, home of the Earl of Pembroke. They were commissioned by the 10th Earl and executed by Baron Reis d'Eisenberg, Riding Master at the Court of the Hapsburgs under Charles VI and Francis I. Dating from the eighteenth century, they show that 'coloured horses' were prized by the aristocracy, and particularly by royalty. Fifteen of the fifty-five pictures representing actual horses known to the artist, some of which are identified by name, place of birth

A spotted blanket on a horse said to be of Danish blood. Detail from a painting by riding master Baron Reis d'Eisenberg in the eighteenth-century Wilton House collection.

and trainer, are what might be termed 'odd coloured'. Three are duns, three are piebald (black and white, one being a black tobiano, and two black with overo markings), and four skewbald (chestnut with white overo markings). There are five distinct Appaloosas with the coat patterns as we recognize them today. The markings are not stylized, as in depictions prior to this age, but very revealing. They comprise one chestnut with a loud white blanket containing darker spots; one dark grey with a very large lighter grey blanket and very large black spots (this horse was of Danish

11

Detail from Baron Reis d'Eisenberg's painting of a leopard spot reared at the Imperial Stud of Bohemia, in the Wilton House collection.

blood); and a grey with a few large irregular spots over the entire body – a few-spot leopard. This horse also has a chestnut varnished rump with chestnut marks on flank and chest. The spots on all three horses are double ringed, being dense inner spots haloed with a pale grey. The few-spot leopard was trained at the Austrian State School by Trainer de Regenthal, who leased it to Count de Langheim for a carousel performance where it was killed by accident. From the seventeenth century onwards carousels took the place of the earlier Gestech joust, which was not intended to be lethal. On this occasion the rider had to pay the horse's value of the equivalent of £10,000 – quite a sum for a horse and a figure that would not be matched for an Appaloosa until well into the last quarter of the twentieth century. The last two Appaloosas in the Wilton collection are distinct leopards, one showing a lighter concentration of spots, especially on the neck, and the other a slightly darker grey with a profusion of large black spots evenly distributed over the entire body. This horse carries the Imperial Brand and was foaled at the Royal Stud in Bohemia.

Nearly a century later and on a much more bitter field, the Peninsular Wars were fought with Spain and England ranged against Napoleon. Horses suffered incredible hardships, as we are told by Lieutenant C. Jones of the 15th Hussars in his diary of the Corunna campaign. Spanish prisoners, held in Denmark under the French Marshal Bernadotte, escaped, leaving behind the war spoils of Spanish horses. From amongst them, one spotted mare, Flaebehoppen, when put to a Danish Fredericksborg stallion produced spotted progeny. It is from this stock that the modern Knabstrup breed descends. For the purposes of the Appaloosa story it is also worth noting that horses of Appaloosa coat patterns were bred in the stud at Lipica near Trieste. The painting by Johann Georg Hamilton, court painter to the Hapsburgs in the eighteenth century, shows a vividly marked Appaloosa in the many-coloured herd at the Lipica stud. At this time too the King of Denmark presented a Fredericksborg horse to the Lipica stud. It is not unknown for some Fredericksborgs to have shown spotted markings.

In England too there were many examples of spotted horses, some of Spanish ancestry, some direct imports such as Lady Conway's Spanish Jennet depicted in a

Lady Conway's Spanish Jennet. Detail from an eighteenth-century painting by John Wootton.

painting by Wootton which now hangs at Ragley Hall, the home of the Marquess of Hertford. This horse shows extreme refinement and a very loud leopard coat.

The Nez Percé Indians

At this chronological point we must cross to the New World, the Americas, where the horse got its modern name, Appaloosa. Yet even here we cannot leave Spain behind for she sent her horses to the Americas and had studs in the Antilles, and the frequent incursions of Conquistadores took place mounted either on first generation Spanish stock, or on horses born at the Antillean studs. From the escaped and captured horses of these conquerors and their later descendants sprang the ancestors of the nineteenth-century range horses of the American West and South West. At this time the Nez Percé Indians, who live in the Columbia Basin in Washington Territory, enter the picture. Their history is interwoven with that of the Appaloosa. It is to this tribe's understanding of genetic principles that the modern Appaloosa owes much of its fabled toughness, ability and class.

The Nez Percé was the only tribe to practice culling, selective breeding, and the gelding of substandard colts. They first acquired the horse in the early eighteenth century and gradually this prized possession enabled them to change their way of life from sedentary farming to nomadic hunting. As a result of these enlightened breeding practices – with both solid and coloured horses, for not all the Nez Percé horses were coloured – the white settlers turned covetous eyes towards this stock. These animals were unusually large for Indian horses, standing 15 hands and better and with a much heavier build, but withal refined.

It was on this sturdy stock that the Nez Percé made their epic flight in 1877 in a bid for freedom. They almost succeeded, but at the end, because of a misconception about the exact border with Canada, and believing the US Cavalry to be at least two days' march away, they rested up to give both the tribe and their horses much needed time for recuperation. The newly installed telegraph line was their ultimate undoing, enabling reinforcements to the cavalry to be summoned. The Indians were trapped, and after fighting a desperate but losing battle were forced back on to the Lapwai Reservation in Idaho. They were also forced back into farming, their horses were confiscated and hundreds of the animals shot on cavalry orders. Those few that survived were ordered to be crossed with cold-blooded draught horses, thus destroying a lifetime's work of upgrading the stock.

Some pockets of Nez Percé horses escaped the slaughter and the downgrading because there had been insufficient time to gather all the animals before the trek. Of the solid-coloured stock no record has come down, but the spotted horse has made his mark over the years, in the process acquiring the name by which he is now known worldwide. Initially he was called a Palouse horse from the area in which he was raised and through which the Palouse River ran. In time this became corrupted into the modern breed name Appaloosa.

So where does this leave us in regard to the horse that is now called the Appaloosa in most countries, with some few spotted breeds like the Knabstrup still keeping its own name, yet originally, even hundreds of years ago, stemming from the same stock? Spain is the obvious catalyst in the days of recorded history, especially equestrian history. Yet prior to that Spain too had her incursions, and for these we must look even further back: to the days of the Carthaginians, who employed mercenary troops, both foot and horse, and held much of Spain below the Ebro; and to the Romans, who held the upper half of Spain as well as much of Asia Minor. In the early Christian era, when Rome expanded her cavalry she used many of the equestrian nations to flesh out her cavalry *alae* and *cohors equitatae*. To the *alae* alone Spain provided the second largest contingent of 6,000 men, while Lugdunum (Lyons) gave 13,000, Thrace (Greece/Bulgaria) 4,500, Pannonia (Hungary and Yugoslavia) 4,000, and other nations such as Syria and Africa 2,000 each. Add to these the reinforcements and subsequent levies and the figures expand. Many of these areas have yielded spotted artefacts, as detailed in the early part of this chapter. Spain (which then included Portugal) in Roman times consisted of three Roman provinces – Baetica, Lusitania and Tarraconensis – and horses were bred for the track and for cavalry. *Alae* were sent on long-distance postings, and thus one of the main melting pots for horseflesh became Spain. Celtic (including Celtiberian) warriors provided much of the cavalry for both sides in the Hannibalic wars, and later Caesar sent into Spain for horses for his cavalry, and it is known that Germanicus stripped Gaul (France) of all available horses for his Germanic wars. Spain had her indigenous breeds, but she also had her own imports, either from straightforward trade, or – most definitely – from the constant incursions during the warring days of Carthaginian power, followed by the centuries-long occupation by Roman legions and their cavalry *alae*. These in turn were followed by Moslem incursions and an input of new blood from Moorish horses. It seems almost certain, therefore, that the Appaloosa colouring did stem from Asia and was then disseminated to other areas throughout this historical period.

3 Breed evolution and societies

The formation of breeds

Homer was one of the first writers to note actual breed characteristics when he described the white Thracian, chestnut Pthians, slow Pylians, and the famous horses of Tros out of Laomedan's mares – all these from lands known to and/or occupied by the ancient Greeks. Sophocles went further, naming teams and breeds racing at the Delphi festival where Orestes was killed in a chariot smash. Two of the nine teams were from Libya, the rest from the Greek mainland. Herodotus of Halicarnassus mentions the Libyans again in his description of Xerxes' massive army of foot and horse that included 10,000 elite Persian cavalry on Nesean horses. Medes and Cashites formed mounted archer spearman units, and mounted archers came from the Caspian, India, Bactria and Paricania. This military juggernaut rolled up the Royal Road to Greece in Xerxes' ill-fated war that ended in bloody defeat at Plateae in 479 BC. The Persians had mustered 35,000 infantry, 12,000 cavalry and 15,000 disaffected Greeks, amongst them crack Thessalian cavalry. Of this number 30,000 fell, thus leaving a mass of new horseflesh to enter into the European mainland. In Arabia too we hear of early horses from two sources: Strabo, a first-century BC geographer, gives a confused tale of an influx and return of equines coming across the Erythraean Sea (Persian Gulf) well before his own time; and Aristarchus of Samothrace mentions Erembian horses in the late third or early second century BC. Oppian talks of Erembi as being in Arabia Felix. We know that bones of domesticated horses found in Asia Minor date to 2,000 BC, and recent finds in Arabia have yielded fossilized bones from ten million years ago. This coupled with the constant incursions of conquerors and the migratory peregrinations of nomadic peoples squarely sets first Asia Minor and then Europe as a melting pot for the foundation stock of what we now know as individual breeds of horse.

Some of this foundation stock was what we term 'hot blood' from arid territories, and eventually developed into horses of a refined and very tough makeup, well able to withstand the dessication that movement in such territory entails. Others from the outer reaches of the Persian Empire – Bactria, Scythia and the steppe lands – had developed into tougher horses suited to a nomad's way of life. In their peregrinations this stock naturally interbred with the animals indigenous to the thousands of miles and hundreds of years that their migrations covered. The horses owned by steppe

16

dwellers were not necessarily small. Burials from the fifth century BC of proto-Sarmations at Pazyryk in the Altai Mountains of central Asia have yielded horses of small steppe pony conformation and larger refined animals of 15 hands plus. They have also yielded artefacts from China and Persia, thus proving that trading took place. The elite would have traded for horses very early on, and ancient annals frequently recount such transactions, sometimes as purchases, sometimes as tribute or even gifts. At that time Persia was already noted for its huge Nesean horses. Much later Tacitus tells us that only Sarmatian nobles' horses were armoured, indicating a larger weight-carrier than the horses of lesser troops.

Thus by the time Herodotus set down the first universal history, the ancestors of our modern horses had acquired two very important attributes: refinement and toughness. Further migrants, the Celts in particular, came into Europe and brought their livestock with them. Once in Europe breeds again interbred, acquiring much of the heavier 'cold-blooded' characteristics of equines resident in the colder and wetter zones. Constant upgrading and infusions of desired 'hot blood' for both the racetrack and army were conducted. Vegetius specifically tells us that African (Libyan) horses were crossed on to Spanish stock to inject speed. From these times come the repeated definitions of horses classified according to breed by a diversity of writers.

Breeds are usually known by their specific locality, whether it be area, country or even stud. Some few are known by the name of the person mainly responsible for developing the breed, such as in modern times the Morgan and the Moyle. Yet others are classified by their markings or their uses.

The spotted breed has been variously labelled in different countries, but the name by which he is commonly known around the world today is Appaloosa, and most associations administering a registry for stock of such breeding either incorporate the word Appaloosa into their title, or describe their association's business as maintaining a registry of horses of Appaloosa breeding. Good specimens of this breed still maintain the strong traits that have stamped it down the centuries, namely toughness, with a hardiness of hoof essential in a horse used in ancient long-range conquests; enough quality to give an efficient and pleasing conformation, but allied with just enough 'cold blood' to ensure tractability and economy of energy. The distinctive coat patterns stemming from especially strong colour genes have also come through in all their variety. Some breeders consider this a welcome bonus, others the main aim. Indeed, as a true breed some Appaloosas do not show definite breed colour yet still carry the genes that may well produce high colour in their offspring. Although there is controversy over the matter of 'solid colour' Appaloosas versus conventional coloured Appaloosas, by blood the solid-coloured animals are counted as members of the breed in registries for Appaloosas. These two sections of the same breed are catered for under different sets of rules in the ApHC and the British Appaloosa Society (BApS). These rules generally dictate which section of a particular registry the animal is in and its rights to be shown in breed competition. It is one of the main differences that separate various registries.

The Appaloosa Horse Club

The registry which is the parent body for many of the other national registries, including France, Italy, Belgium, Canada, Mexico, New Zealand and Australia, is the Appaloosa Horse Club, Inc., of Moscow, Idaho, USA.

This association is now a vast organization governing the public performances of many Appaloosa horse operations throughout the world. The Appaloosa also claims to be the third most popular breed in the USA. The ApHC had its very small beginnings in 1938 when Claude J. Thompson, an Oregon farmer with a lifelong passion for good horses, especially Appaloosas, realized the need to gather available records on good Appaloosas before all traces of individuals' recorded history was lost. At that time these highly coloured horses were in a real minority, and in danger of being totally absorbed into the general pool of what the Americans call 'grade' or unregistered horses, their blood so diffused that breed characteristics would eventually be irreversibly weakened and the Appaloosa become truly the horse of Indian legend.

Claude had first been introduced to Appaloosas as a young boy, and began breeding them in the 1920s. At the same time he also owned horses of other breeds and was particularly drawn to the Arabian for his beauty. He saw his ideal horse as a cross between an Appaloosa and a superior Arabian, the offspring acquiring the better points of both and advertising its colour heritage by distinct Appaloosa markings. Even before forming the Appaloosa registry he had been steadily working towards pedigreed stock, initially breeding from an Appaloosa stallion named Old Painter, and carrying the line on mainly through his daughters. The desired infusion of Arabian blood came with the purchase of Ferras, a purebred chestnut colt. The resultant crosses of the Old Painter and Ferras blood, including linebreeding to Ferras, was to produce some of the best of the earliest registered horses. It also gave the Appaloosa much refinement. Additionally it complemented the Appaloosa's known attributes of hardiness, endurance and durable hooves. Claude Thompson believed strongly in using outcrossing with great care, preferring to use purebred Arabians, and when this was not possible to use either Thoroughbred or Morgan horses who showed some Arabian characteristics.

Apart from feeling Arabian outcrosses were desirable, another reason for originally using so much outside blood in the formative years of the Appaloosa registry was because there were insufficient Appaloosas left in the country from which to draw on without deleterious effects. Claude Thompson's breeding acumen was proved beyond a doubt as a succession of National Champions stemmed from horses either bred by him or from stock tracing back to his preferred bloodlines. One of the earliest of these was Red Eagle, National Champion stallion in 1951. He was by Ferras out of Painter's Marvel, a granddaughter of both Ferras and Old Painter. He was followed by his sons who also won the championship: American Eagle in 1953 and Red Eagle's Peacock in 1956. Their descendants feature prominently in major American show records down the years.

Working alongside Claude Thompson in this important time of resurgence was Dr Francis Haines, a historian who in his early years had herded cattle in Montana. This was a fortuitous combination of historian and horseman. Dr Haines' doctoral thesis was on the history of the Nez Percé Indians, and it was during his research studies that frequent references to the horses bred by the tribe caught his imagination. A story told by celebrated Western artist Charles Russell was the catalyst for his further research into the history of the Appaloosa horse. The partnership of Dr Haines, newly graduated from the University of California at Berkeley, and Claude Thompson began to open the media doors and led to national press coverage for the Appaloosa breed. Here was a horse story with a difference – a proven part of America's heritage being rescued from oblivion. To these two men the modern Appaloosa owes an immeasurable debt.

The first few years of the new registry were lean, with only a handful of paid-up members and 113 horses being registered. By 1947 another major milestone was reached with the publication of the first stud book, followed in 1950 by the acceptance of the Appaloosa as a breed by the National Association of Stallions Registration Board in Chicago. This was undoubtedly the most momentous achievement for the pioneering triumvirate of Claude Thompson, Dr Haines and George Hatley, the association secretary, who had spearheaded the reintroduction and popularization of an almost lost breed. This acceptance also entitled Appaloosas to enter open and all-breed shows, and was the launching pad for the upsurge in Appaloosa popularity that made great strides in the 1950s.

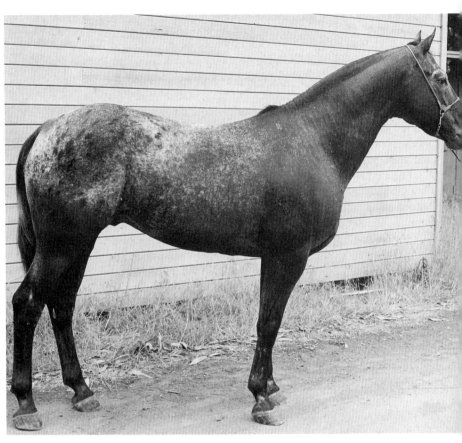

An excellent type of early registered American Appaloosa, Little Bull by the famous Joker B. He combines strength and elegance with all the Appaloosa characteristics.

With the increased leisure, finance and security following the war years, breeding horses for pleasure, and by many for profit, escalated so that the ApHC was handling thousands of registrations a year. Since then the association has grown by leaps and bounds and is now a multi-million dollar financial enterprise dealing with every aspect of the American Appaloosa horse from registering the stock to governing the many activities in which this colourful horse is to be found competing.

There are sections for racing and showing Appaloosas, and the ApHC also encourages Appaloosa participation in many open competitive fields, the most notable of which must be endurance riding where many Appaloosas have excelled. They also shine in open jumping divisions, where they compete against the best, and in Western reining, where they more than hold their own against the specialist Quarter Horse. Dressage is also a field where they are making their mark, both in America and in Britain. However, the American stronghold for Appaloosas is in the tremendous variety of Western performance classes. This is particularly so since repeated and heavy infusions of Quarter Horse blood, particularly in recent years, have resulted in the type of horse more suited to these activities than to English-orientated performance. Nevertheless, with such a numerous breed there is ample room for diversification and Appaloosas of a more Thoroughbred type of conformation, often achieved with direct outcrossing to the Thoroughbred, are the other side of the coloured coin.

The numerical strength of the breed has necessitated distinct divisions being organized for the many thousands of owners and horses who compete on a regular basis. At grass roots level Appaloosas carry the breed flag in the countless shows around the United States and Canada, competing in classes open to all horses as well as those restricted to their own breed. To offer competition under the auspices of the ApHC the country is divided into five territories, each subdivided into three zones. These cater for the well over 200 regional clubs offering a variety of activities centred around the Appaloosa horse. They include showing, trail rides, educational seminars and clinics, and they also promote the breed through many other means. The ApHC itself holds several major shows a year where the best in the nation compete. The National Appaloosa Show originally shifted its venue each year to give all members the chance of having it more in their own territory once in a while. Current practice is to hold it at Albuquerque, New Mexico, in alternate years, and have it peripatetic in the interim year. The World Championship Show for halter and performance horses is an annual event, and the third major show is the Appaloosa Cutting Horse Maturity, Futurity, Matched Roping and Heading and Heeling Tournament for the true Western performance athletes.

The ApHC also promotes overseas interest in the breed and many other countries have imported considerable numbers of American Appaloosas as the foundation stock for their studs. For example, Japan has imported them just to fill a gap in the

21

booming market for pleasure riding in that country, Appaloosas forming over a quarter of the consignment of fifty horses exported to Japan in the early 1980s. The Appaloosa is thriving in Mexico, Brazil, Australia and New Zealand, and in the past few years many of the European countries have started their own Appaloosa associations under the aegis of the ApHC and following their rulings on registration, show and performance formats. The ApHC has sent its own representative to foreign countries on promotional tours, and occasionally an ApHC registered judge is able to officiate at the European Appaloosa shows.

Other American Appaloosa groups

In addition to the ApHC there are many other societies in the USA which cater to afficionados of the Appaloosa horse. Three of these groups are devoted to preserving the bloodlines of some of the most famous of the early foundation horses such as Red Eagle, Sundance and Toby. The Colorado Ranger Horse Association, while not being either a colour registry or a specifically Appaloosa orientated association, nevertheless has up to 90 per cent of its horses double registered with the ApHC. There are two associations registering Appaloosa ponies. These are the National Appaloosa Pony, Inc., which was formed in 1963, and the Pony of the Americas Club which was started in 1955. Ponies up to 14 hands high are eligible to be registered in either association. Finally the newest of the Appaloosa organizations is the Appaloosa Color Breeders Association, started in 1983 by a group of people dedicated to preserving the Appaloosa as a uniquely distinctive breed complete with the traditional identifying characteristics. Its registration requirements differ markedly from the modern rules applying to ApHC regulations, being more in line with the characteristics and colour demanded for horses prior to 1983 if they were to enjoy full benefits including the right to show in Appaloosa competition.

European registries

In the late 1970s the Appaloosa horse began to become very popular in Europe and several European nations formed their own Appaloosa societies. Some are under the direct aegis of the ApHC, others are not. Germany has a strong nucleus of Appaloosa horses, most now with strong infusions of Quarter Horse blood as that breed is extremely popular in Germany at present. The emergence of the Germans as an Appaloosa-owning horse people stemmed from the 1975 Equitana when ten horses from Indiana were exhibited at this prestigious equestrian trade fair which is held every second year at Essen. Most of the exhibited horses found new ownership in German stables, and in 1978 the Germans started their own official registry, limiting the horses eligible to those with either American or Canadian registrations.

Klaus, one of the most successful horses in the Appaloosa show ring, is an imported stallion whose dam Musse is registered in the Dutch society.

Holland also has its own Appaloosa Society which does not come under the wing of the ApHC. Unlike most of the other Appaloosa associations it has two sections to its registry, one for animals with pony breeding, the other for horses.

Denmark

The Knabstrup has been briefly mentioned in Chapter 1. Denmark has the world's oldest registry for spotted horses, dating to 1933 when the Danish society was first formed and covered Zealand, Falster, Lolland and Funen. In 1971 the Society went national, incorporating the mainland of Jutland. The modern Knabstrup has gone through many vicissitudes, as has the American Appaloosa, with much common blood at one time being infused. The modern trend is towards the riding horse of extreme quality, and the Knabstrup is esteemed as an all-around versatility horse.

Any stallion standing at stud must first pass stiff veterinary and performance tests, imposed on most European breeds, showing his capabilities in dressage, jumping and cross country. The quality aimed at is in many respects a return to the origins of the breed, which stems not only from the Spanish Flaebehoppen (*hoppe* = mare), but also on the spear side from the descendants bred at the Royal Frederiksborg Stud in King Christian VI's time. He had a preference for leopard horses, or as they were then termed 'tiger' horses. The first Danish 'tiger' recorded is a stallion foaled in 1671. He was by a Spanish 'tiger' stallion. The leopard horses became popular in royal circles, the king maintaining a select stud, and in 1680 he gave his sister a matched pair of carriage horses. The leopard side of the Frederiksborg stud flourished for nearly a century but was disbanded in 1759. However, the colours did not completely die out, and, just as occasionally a Quarter Horse is an Appaloosa outcrop, the Frederiksborg right down to modern times occasionally produced a horse with such markings.

It was at this time that the Lunn family bought the Knabstrup Estate from which the breed takes its name, though the horses stocked there were not the tiger strain of Frederiksborgs. The Lunns purchased the Flaebe mare, put her to a 'yellow' stallion and in 1813 Flaebehingsten (*hingst* = stallion) was foaled. He had a palomino base coat with a palette of spots thereon: white, chestnut, liver chestnut, brown and black. On his sire's side he traced to two horses of royal descent: the stallion Beaver from the Royal Frederiksborg Stud, and a chestnut mare from another royal stud at Løvenborg. Though the Lunns' early stock was not tiger coloured it may well be that the colour genes had lain dormant, and quite possibly the colour was not solely

24

inherited from the Spanish mare who was herself a roan with small white spots all over and a scattering of a few red spots, more concentrated on her quarters.

The most noted Knabstrup foundation stallion is Old Thor, foaled 1847. Many modern horses trace to this stallion whose pedigree is very interesting. It shows several crosses on both sire and dam's sides to both the original Flaebe mare through her son Flaebehingsten, and to a daughter Flaebe 2, by a premium Jutland stallion, thus intensifying the 'coloured' blood. Additionally there is another cross on his dam's side to another Frederiksborg stallion, thus intensifying this strain as well.

A list of breeding stock from the Knabstrup Stud dated to January 1855 shows two stallions, Old Thor, who was red spotted, and Frode, a brown spotted leopard. Of the sixteen mares mentioned eight were spotted, three red, three black, one dark chestnut, and one brown. Of three full sisters to Old Thor one carried red spots, one black spots, and one was solid coloured. Obviously chance played just as much a part then as now. Of twenty-one foals sired by Thor and Frode, and a single foal by Hamilton, who was by a yellow stallion and out of a yellow mare, and who sired an 'Isabella' (palomino) colt, only seven were coloured. Five of these had both parents spotted, two only the sire. One mare, Kyllingen, had a solid coloured and a spotted foal by Thor in successive years. One other solid foal came from a tiger (leopard) mare. Frode sired three foals of which two were spotted from spotted mares, the rest were by Thor. Appaloosa studs would not be happy with such a ratio today.

Within the modern Knabstrup breed there are recent importations of Canadian and American Appaloosas. The horses having most impact are the stallions Dancan Coco and Dancan Sunspot owned by Henning Klausen of Randbøl. Both these stallions are also registered in the Knabstrup registry.

In common with most Appaloosa associations artificial insemination is permitted, but unlike the American association which currently forbids it, semen can be transported. Outcrossing is permitted but no registered Knabstrup may have more than 50% of outside blood. The breed most used for outcrossing is the Danish Warmblood. There are two sections in the registry. One is for animals up to 148 cm, and one for horses over this height.

A top representative of the breed is Thunder Boy, a black spot leopard by Thundercloud, a Knabstrup stallion, out of Sherie, of Warmblood breeding. He was bred by Ingrid Mikkelsen, a noted Danish breeder of Knabstrup horses who has also worked on the *Knabstrupperforeninge* committee for many years. Thunder Boy was the leading performance Knabstrup for three years prior to accompanying Ingrid's daughter Maj-Britt to England in 1989. His points were mainly gained in show

jumping, dressage and sidesaddle events. In the latter he did a 90-mile sponsored ride from Herning to Århus to raise funds for the Vilhelmsborg Horsesports Centre and he is pictured with Maj-Britt in eighteenth-century costume.

(Opposite page)

The Knabstrup stallion Thunder Boy, shown in historical costume in Denmark by Maj-Britt Carter.

4 Great Britain

Britain has two distinct breed registries for spotted equines. These are the British Appaloosa Society and the British Spotted Pony Society. Both were founded in 1976, but previously there had been one society.

The British Spotted Horse and Pony Society which dates to 1946 was formed to establish a register of all spotted equines in Britain. As time passed, and particularly because of the very strong impression the Appaloosa was making in America, it became evident there was a need for two distinct societies each catering for specfic animals. Most of the characteristics found in Appaloosas are also found in both the ponies and horses registered in these societies, the main difference being the use of pony blood as a requirement in the Spotted Pony Society and the prohibition of its use in the Appaloosa Society.

First years of the British Appaloosa Society

The British Appaloosa Society owes an immeasurable debt to one family, and one mare. Desmie and Ken de Rivaz owned a leopard spotted Argentinian mare called Petrukas, whom they decided to send to probably the only registered Appaloosa stallion in the country when she had finished her prime role as a polo pony. This stallion was Sunrise Speckled Hawk owned by Colonel V. D. S. Williams who had a small stud of imported Canadian Appaloosas at his home at Farnham Royal in Buckinghamshire. He was a very enthusiastic promoter of the breed in Britain many years before the BApS was founded.

It was this mating between Petrukas and Sunrise Speckled Hawk that produced not only the hoped for spotted foal, the near-leopard Rivaz Burletta, but an interest that eventually came to dominate both the de Rivaz's lives, as well as that of their talented daughter Anne who has done so much not only to campaign the de Rivaz's horses successfully, but in doing so to promote the breed in general.

Petrukas was both the foundation mare in the British stud book, bearing the number F1, and the de Rivaz's foundation mare. By 1976 the stud had expanded with several of Petrukas' progeny and other purchased horses forming a sizeable group at Woodcock Lodge Farm, Tylers Causeway, in Hertfordshire.

There were several other breeders of Appaloosas in the country by now, most notably Nigel and Lucia Boase in Argyllshire, Scotland, and on 21 September 1976

Foundation mare of the British Appaloosa Society, the Rivaz Stud's Petrukas with foal.

the inaugural meeting to form the British Appaloosa Society was held. It started with two advantages to add to the enthusiasm of its twenty-seven founder members, namely the blessing and sanction of the British Horse Society and, more importantly at that time, the good wishes of the Appaloosa Horse Club of America.

In December of the same year a steering committee was formed to guide the new society through its early days. In addition to Ken and Desmie de Rivaz it was spearheaded by its first President, Raymond Brooks-Ward, MFH, who gave much encouragement and a tremendous amount of practical help in the early years. Through his efforts and position in the British equestrian world the Appaloosa horse was quickly able to make itself known to the wider British audience, with an original and very colourful parade of ten Appaloosas at the 1976 Christmas International Show at Olympia. Fulfilling the dual role of showing the breed's visible characteristics to the public and of advertising that here were horses eminently suited to any of the British areas of activity, each horse appeared as a participant in a different performance activity. As it was such a successful effort and made BApS history the programme is worth giving here.

PALEFACE RAMPAGE A leopard stallion driven by his owner Christine Madeira.
TIBERTICH CHACO A liver spot leopard Argentinian stallion ridden by Nigel Boase in Indian costume. His wife Lucia rode Western style on:
TIBERTICH SILVA A 5-year-old leopard mare.
JUST JOE Ridden by Kate Davis as a junior jumper. The other junior element was:
SILVER CLOUD MERRY DANCE A pony club and family horse ridden by Miss Ivey.

The Rivaz stud was well represented and at such an early stage in the breed's public British history they are to be commended on providing such a variety of talent. All except the point-to-point field are events in which British Appaloosas compete successfully.

PENDEAN BOBBY A leopard stallion ridden by daughter Gail in Western show attire.
ASTERISK A leopard mare ridden sidesaddle by Silvia Astley.
APPLEJACK Don Parker's point-to-pointer.
SPOT ON Daughter Anne's cross country eventer, a field where the Appaloosa has been doing very well in Britain.
PETRUKAS Ridden by son Paul in her old role as a polo pony.

During its first year the BApS also had its first American visitor. It so happened that Sharon Saare, who was one of the leading long distance riders in the USA at the time and author of many successful books and articles, several on the Appaloosa horse, was visiting England to compete in a British Competitive Trail Ride. At the time she

(Left)

Spot On, successful cross country with Anne de Rivaz.

(Below)

Paleface Rampage, leopard stallion bred by Christine Madeira and later owned by George Donald of Aberdeen.

was also a key member on the ApHC's staff organizing and instructing on their Distance Riding programme. During her stay in England she combined her riding with a visit to Woodcock Lodge Farm and was able to give on-the-spot advice to the fledgling society. In its formative years the society was also fortunate in gaining recognition and much assistance from such notable horsemen as the late Dorian Williams, MFH, and from Captain Elwyn Hartley Edwards who is the current President and has frequently advised on many important issues.

Though not to be compared numerically with Appaloosas in the USA where horse breeding and showing is on a very much more financially structured basis, the growth of the BApS was rapid. In its first year it attracted 145 members, and 115 horses were registered, and in the next ten years total registrations rose to well over 800. Current expansion is steady and the quality of the animals being bred has also risen dramatically from the early years.

Right from the start Chairman Ken de Rivaz was adamant that well-organized advertising and breed promotion were a vital part of the society's duty in popularizing the breed. This was coupled with the stated aims of the society to 'Improve and preserve the breed of the Appaloosa horse . . . to provide high standards and tangible systems of show judging . . . to hold shows, exhibitions and parades.' To this end Appaloosas began to be seen in many prestigious equestrian events, none more so than the annual Royal Show held at the National Agricultural Centre at Stoneleigh in Warwickshire. Here in 1977 the BApS had a promotion stand manned throughout the whole of the four-day show by BApS members, and on one day by a representative from the ApHC, Mr Len Murray. Subsequently the BApS have had a stand at every Royal Show where the promotion is live through the medium of several top quality Appaloosas on show at the stand, as well as a variety of society literature, coupled with on-the-spot explanations of the many questions potential Appaloosa owners ask.

In 1977 a small event occurred that was to have future favourable consequences for the BApS. Internationally famous singer and musician Paul McCartney bought his first Appaloosa in America. This was the first of many Appaloosas for Paul and Linda McCartney, one of whom, Lucky Spots Blankit, a bay colt with spotted blanket, was shown very successfully at the BApS 1984 National Show. He won second place in

(Opposite page)

Lucky Spots Blankit, pictured (*above*) in the show ring handled by Peter Larrigan, and (*below*) as a foal with owner Linda McCartney.

the Junior Stallion class on his first show outing in the hands of veteran circus showman Peter Larrigan, father of Olympic dressage rider Tanya Larrigan. Linda McCartney has been one of the most generous sponsors of the BApS and the success of the National Show is in large measure due to her frequent underwriting of much of its heavy cost, especially in the first few struggling years.

More prestigious milestones were reached that gave added momentum to the very strong practices of the Steering Committee who were determined to put the Appaloosa on the British equestrian map.

The first National Show was held in 1977, attracting over seventy entries and with a huge entry of thirty coming forward in the Riding Horse class, which was deservedly won by Asterisk ridden by Anne de Rivaz. Asterisk won her in-hand class and was named Female Champion of the show. The Male Champion and also winner of the stallion class was Mr J. Wild's Kingswood Spotted Wonda. Many of this stallion's offspring were exported to Australia. Reserve to him in both events stood the horse that was to have possibly the most influence on the next decade of Appaloosa breeding in Britain. This impact was also felt in many European countries, especially Australia, where his progeny found new homes. The horse was Klaus, a superb brown spot leopard, brought over from Holland where he had already had a very successful in-hand career. He was bought by the Rivaz Stud to stand in England. His career at stud and in Appaloosa and open competition has been largely responsible for the above-mentioned map-making.

Considered to be hugely successful, the first British National Appaloosa Show earnt the society a compliment from ApHC Executive Secretary George Hatley as having attracted more entries than the first one held by the American Society. And incidentally it was a decade before the ApHC held their first national show.

An invitation from the Queen's Equerry, Colonel Sir John Miller, resulted in the BApS participating in a Parade of Rare and Unusual Breeds of Horses in June 1978. To ensure that a high standard of horse went forward to Smith's Lawn, Windsor, home of British polo, horses selected were all winners in events affiliated to BApS. On the day ten Appaloosas, including a tiny foal alongside his dam, were seen by Her Majesty, the Queen, who seemed very impressed and interested in the unusual sight. (I recall the impression it made on me as I was at that time involved with the Quarter

(Opposite page)

Asterisk (*above*), an early Rivaz mare and a top performer, including winner of the Riding Horse class and Female Champion at the first BApS National Show; (*below*) the Appaloosa parade at Smith's Lawn, Windsor, being inspected by HM The Queen.

34

The influential stallion Klaus, jumped by Anne de Rivaz.

Horse contingent in the parade.) The Appaloosas had by far the most impressive and the largest number of horses on show.

Two years after its inauguration, during which time the ApHC in America had given much encouragement, the British Society was fully recognized by this body.

The BApS endorsed and followed the then current ApHC rules for registration and many of the British Appaloosas were able to be fully registered in the ApHC registry as well. But this was not a one-way traffic. With the popularity of the breed expanding in Britain there began to be a small but steady trickle of American Appaloosas imported into Britain. At the same time Britain was finding a market for her Appaloosas on the European continent and in Australia. The Appaloosa breed was indeed completing the round trip started so many hundreds of years ago when the Americans received their first horses from Europe.

The British Spotted Pony Society

The British Spotted Pony Society categorically states that its animals are truly British and are not Appaloosas. This is correct in the modern sense because neither the American nor British Appaloosa Societies permit animals of pony derivation.

However, it is more than a probability that the antecedents of the British Spotted Pony carried true Appaloosa genes in exactly the same way that the American Appaloosa inherited his – that is, through Spain, and prior to that from Asia Minor. Britain was the recipient of Spanish horses well before medieval times. Many of the Roman cavalry units were mounted on Hispanic horses, and the Spanish influence was of course re-introduced in medieval, Tudor, and later Carolingian times when many of the war horses and later the high school horses, a number of which were spotted, were of Spanish blood.

A parchment dated 1298 listing cavalry expenses for Edward I's Falkirk campaign describes a Robin Fitzpayne's spotted Welsh horse valued at 25 marks (£16.13s.4d). This was a considerable value for a horse in those days, as any study of the Pipe Rolls of the period will show. It also places the spots as belonging to a Welsh horse, presumably of the type we know today as a cob. Spots have been one of the characteristics of a pony, known as the Blagdon, raised in Wales up until recent times.

Apart from the required characteristics of Appaloosa type, which are covered separately, the British Spotted Pony Society's registration regulations accepts ponies of riding or driving, including cob, type up to a height limit of 14.2 hh. Any piebald or skewbald markings make the pony ineligible for registration. Ponies must have two or more generations of correct, registered breeding, and parents and grandparents must be registered with the British Spotted Pony Society or the previous British Spotted Horse and Pony Society. However, the stud book is still open to certain outcrosses: ponies registered with the National Pony Society; the Shetland Pony Stud Book Society; the Dartmoor Pony Society; the Fell Pony Society; the Dales Pony Society; the Exmoor Pony Society; and the Welsh Pony and Cob Society, Sections A, B and C. Stallions used must have either the licence formerly issued by the Ministry of Agriculture, or a licence issued by the British Spotted Pony Society. Solid-colour ponies of spotted lineage may be entered in a breeding register but may not enter shows or exhibitions run by the society.

The society encourages its members to prove the versatility of their spotted ponies by running a performance award scheme, and one of the most successful teams of ponies of recent years is that driven by Karen Basset, whose leopard spotted ponies have done very well in open driving competitions.

5 Appaloosa characteristics and registries

Of all the breed's characteristics the one that shouts most loudly is the horse's coat pattern. Basically this falls into two main categories: leopard and blanket. Three other kinds of basic pattern complete the palette: marble, snowflake and frost markings. Within these five patterns there are subdivisions and within these again an infinite variety. No two Appaloosas are ever marked the same. To complicate matters there are also Appaloosas that have no coat pattern whatsoever but do have other Appaloosa characteristics, and even more bewildering there are some that show none of the above, being completely solid coloured, yet are of Appaloosa breeding. This factor has given rise to a tremendous amount of controversy within some of the breed's associations, and is the main point of divergence when it comes to the type of papers the animal is issued with, and what privileges are conferred upon it. Both sides of the argument have valid points to put forward, as noted later in this chapter.

Conformation ideals

The overall appearance of the Appaloosa should be symmetrical. The head should be straight and lean, ears pointed and medium sized. Lips, muzzle, nostrils and the area around the eyes generally show parti-coloured skin. The eyes should preferably be dark, although there is no discrimination against registering an animal with blue eyes. Eyes should be surrounded with white sclera. The neck should show quality, with a clean-cut throat latch and large windpipe. The chest should be deep, shoulders well muscled, long and sloping, and withers well defined. The back is short and straight, loin short and wide, quarters well rounded. The underline is long with the flank well let down. Hips are long, sloping and muscular, running into muscular long thighs; gaskins are also long, wide and muscular, and hocks are clearly defined, wide and straight. Forelegs should be straight, and from the front a perpendicular line should run from point of shoulder through knee, cannon, pastern and hoof. From the side a perpendicular line should run from the centre of the elbow joint through knee, pastern and fetlock joints to the back of the hoof. The hind legs should have a perpendicular line from the quarter through the centre of the hock, cannon, pastern and foot. From the side a perpendicular line should fall from the hip joint to the centre of the hoof, dividing the gaskin. A perpendicular line from the point of the quarter should run parallel with the line of the cannon bone. There is no maximum height, and different associations have minimum height rules. Weight should be proportional to height.

Colour Patterns

Leopard

The leopard patterning usually consists of black or chestnut spots on a white or light-coloured base coat. The spots can range from an inch to four or five inches across, and can be of any shape. They are distributed at random over the entire body, often with a somewhat larger and/or more concentrated patterning over the hindquarters. Some horses have a thick clustering of spots, others more moderate concentrations, and yet others have very few spots. The latter are known as 'few-spot' leopards.

Blanket

These Appaloosas come in two main categories: the completely white rump with the rest of the body solid coloured, or the white rump sprinkled with an irregular patterning of spots. The blanket can cover just the rump, extend to cover the loin and part of the belly and flank, or even reach as far forward as the wither. It is not uncommon for foals with a spotted blanket eventually to 'colour in' as a leopard Appaloosa, or a near leopard. The spots on both leopard and blanket Appaloosas can frequently be felt as raised above the base coat. Some types of spots have a halo effect, which are sometimes known as peacock spots. Other blanket markings resemble white lace on a darker base colour. The lace markings do not extend as far as other blankets.

Marble

Appaloosas coloured thus are usually of either red or blue roan base colour. They frequently have varnish marks – a concentration of darker hairs – on the face, elbows, girth, stifle and hip areas. They may also have a few spots irregularly distributed. Such a horse may start life marbled and 'colour out' to a few-spot leopard (see p. 109). In the marbled classification horses with a grey base coat also appear. They must not be confused with the blue roan base colour. In some registries such a

True leopard colouring, where the foal is born leopard and carries the spots throughout its life.

Near leopard, with solid-coloured face and legs.

Few spot leopard. The solid colours will gradually disappear with age.

Spotted blanket on Merely Diandz. Compare the adult horse on p. 77.

Lace blanket, on a foal which later became roan.

Marbled Appaloosa with a red roan base colour.

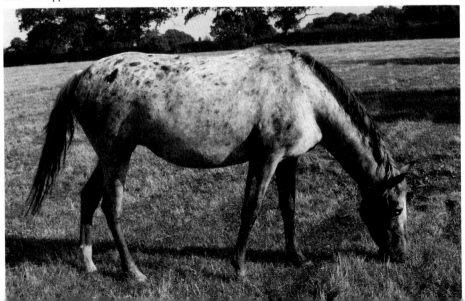

Varnish marks on the nose of a horse which has 'coloured out' to a few spot leopard.

grey base colour would make the animal ineligible for registration. This is another point where registries differ.

Snowflake

The snowflake pattern is the apparent reverse of leopard, with the base coat dark and dusted with white flakes resembling snow. However, these flakes or spots are usually not as clear in outline as the hard edged leopard variety. This patterning should not

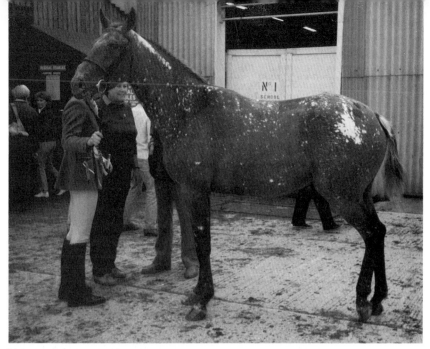

The snowflake pattern is the least common Appaloosa colouring.

be mistaken for grey horses that also sometimes have a snowflake patterned coat. The most famous example of this is the British racehorse The Tetrarch. Such grey snowflake horses do not have other Appaloosa characteristics.

Frosted

The frosted Appaloosa has a dark base coat colour and either a light sprinkling of frost or small snowflakes on hip, rump and loin which may extend forwards in the manner of a blanket.

Other characteristics

To be considered an Appaloosa for most registries, the horse must also exhibit some of the following, with differences according to registry. A white sclera surrounds the eye. This is the most noticeable of the characteristics. There should be mottled skin on the muzzle, around the eyes and in the genital area. The hooves are often striated

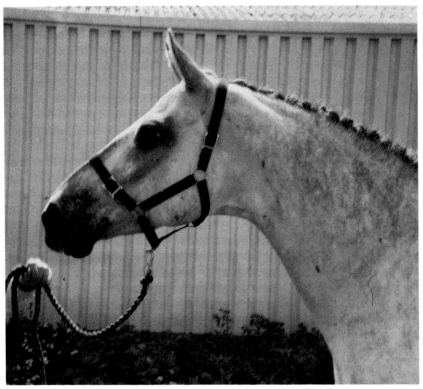

Appaloosa characteristics: white sclera and mottled skin.

with bands of dark and pale coloured laminae. Appaloosa horses are noted for the superior quality of the hoof horn. The last visible characteristic is that some horses have a very sparse mane and tail, although most are well endowed.

As a performance horse the Appaloosa is credited with versatility, tractability, and most of all exceptional hardiness and endurance. The last two characteristics enabled the modern Appaloosa's ancestors to withstand the constant hardships in the days when harassment of the Nez Percé peoples drove them from their homelands. At that time too these horses were singled out from other Indian-bred horses for inherent quality. Much of this quality was lost when, in order to prevent the Nez

Appaloosa characteristics: striated hooves.

Percé from ever being a mounted threat again, draught blood was forcibly introduced into the offspring of the remaining Appaloosa horses. Fortunately some did escape the net of this degradation of type and early dilution of quality Appaloosa blood. However, when the Appaloosa re-emergence occurred and was actively promoted by Claude Thompson and Dr Francis Haines many of the remaining Appaloosas did have a legacy of 'common' blood to combat. It was with the intention of upgrading these animals that select outcrosses of Arabian and Thoroughbred were used in the early days.

In Britain, Australia, Canada and the USA no outcrossing is permitted to ponies or animals possessing pony blood; to horses of paint, piebald or albino colouring; or to horses of heavy draught blood. Britain also prohibits outcrosses to horses of 'vanner' breeding. This is a type found in Britain and is a cobby sort of horse with high rounded action showing his heavy harness horse background. Australia also bars Standardbred blood.

British Appaloosas must measure 14.2 hh at five years of age. As Britain has many pony breeds and the larger of these, such as Fell, Dale, Connemara, New Forest, Highland and Welsh Cob (Section D), frequently measure up to 14.2 hh, a close check on distant pedigrees is kept, and should an animal be found to have pony blood after registration none of its offspring would be eligible for registration and its own papers may be rescinded. The Australians, Canadians and Americans accept animals of 14 hands upwards, as do the societies affiliated to the ApHC.

Another area where registries differ is in the use of grey horses. The British and Australian registries do not permit animals with a grey base coat colour to be registered, nor the progeny of grey horses, because of the fading factor in such horses. There is a 50 per cent chance that stock with one or both parents grey, even if born with Appaloosa coat patterns on a dark base coat, will lose all Appaloosa colour in a very short time, in some cases as early as a year old.

Breed registries

Before discussing the regulations of various Appaloosa breed registries it might be as well to discuss what actually makes a breed, and the progression from there to the importance of a pedigreed horse.

First of all the establishment of a breed takes place over many decades if not centuries, and usually occurs when certain characteristics of a particular strain are noticed for their usefulness to man. Such use can be either as a horse with intrinsic beauty, or more likely as a utilitarian animal that fulfils certain criteria beneficial to man.

The next step is to capitalize on these characteristics, breeding from a nucleus of horses possessing the desired traits, utilizing the best breeding animals, especially stallions which can impart their genetic strength many times per season, until the nucleus has expanded sufficiently and has intensified the characteristics by observant and critical use of the most prepotent animals. Then other animals can be brought in as outcrosses to prevent too much inbreeding, subsequently crossing back to the original lines that carry the strongly desired traits.

Going back in history to the days of the Roman Empire, we find horses that had achieved this breed status in Europe and Asia Minor. They became known for their suitability for war, racing or ceremonial use. Thus we have the white Phrygian horses used on state and ceremonial occasions in Rome and other large Roman cities, and mentioned in the Theodosian Code of laws, compiled in the fifth century but relating to earlier laws of Constantine and his successors. Then there were the Spanish horses long known for war and racing; the ugly white Thracian battle horses; huge Thessalian chargers; incomparable Nesean horses for war and riding, but no good for racing. The agile, swift, tough, small Libyan horses, progenitors of the modern Arabian, were most useful as war horses and racehorses, and were also used extensively to outcross on other breeds, most notably to inject speed into the Spanish, according to a writer on horse breeding and veterinary matters, Publius Vegetius Renatus. Strabo, the first century BC geographer, talks about the breed of horse known as the 'Wolf Breed', raised by the Heneti in olden times (olden to him), but which had completely disappeared as a breed due to repeated outcrossing by his time. They say there is nothing new under the sun, and the maxim still holds good today: dilute the blood too much and the old breed will disappear.

Pedigrees are really the records of the legitimate ancestors of a registered horse, and the purer the ancestors the better the pedigree. This is qualified by the record these ancestors had either for performance or for imparting certain beneficial, or otherwise, characteristics. Study of pedigrees can tell you much of what a foal's ancestors could do, where they came from, what their dispositions were like, and which were the most dominant characteristics. It gives some indication of what to expect as the foal matures into a horse old enough to be used as a riding animal, and later if destined for breeding what it will produce in its own offspring.

The modern Appaloosa nearly always started with one Appaloosa and one 'other' parent and built from there. The BApS is as yet rather young to have detailed and far-reaching records of which line endows which family of horses with recognizable traits. It also has not had time to establish a wide enough base of non-related animals within the breed registry. The ApHC, on the other hand, has a much longer recorded history, by nearly forty years, and strove hard in its early years to establish the Appaloosa horse, of necessity upgrading with outcrosses, but also intensifying the percentage of Appaloosa breeding. It has also had the opportunity to establish a sufficiently large genetic pool to obviate the necessity for continual heavy outcrossing. The British lines have yet to reach the stage where it is possible to close the stud book.

However, as the American body was relaxing its rules by permitting unlimited outcrossing with Thoroughbred, Quarter Horse and Arabian horses, as well as widening the scope for performance by horses of non-Appaloosa appearance, the British registry tightened its laager and introduced a grading system which can only be beneficial to the true Appaloosa in the long run. The Australians, although permitting outcrosses to many breeds, have such tough rules in the areas of conformation, required characteristics, and inherited defects, that any horse going forward to a breeding programme will not perpetuate such deviations from the norm. In their advertising some Australian breeders also state whether their Appaloosa stallions carry Thoroughbred, Quarter Horse or Arabian blood, thus saving prospective owners much uncertainty over the type inheritance of future foals. Later I include a resume of the pertinent sections of their rules which seem to me to be not only for the good of the breed, but also the most encompassing of all the registries. As with their Endurance Ride rules the Australians have gone to the heart of the matter and come up with a clearcut and eminently practical association framework.

Britain

I quote below the BApS registration rules together with detailed explanations of them. In order to understand fully why the grading-up scheme was introduced, it must be explained that the Ministry of Agriculture will not recognize the society as having an official stud book until there are a minimum of three generations shown. It also requires that at least 10 per cent of the stud book be comprised of non-related animals.

Prior to 17 April 1988, the British society had three registries: the Tentative, Permanent, and Breeding Stock Registers. Horses in the Tentative Register conformed to accepted Appaloosa colourings and also had white sclera around the eye and mottled skin in appropriate areas. To pass to the Permanent Register a stallion had to have sired twelve coloured foals and a mare to have produced three coloured foals. Coloured foals of Permanent Registered parents also held

(Opposite page)

Registration certificate of the British Appaloosa Society. The reverse of the card gives full four-generation pedigree, including the colour of the first three generations, and there is also room for transfers to be recorded.

CERTIFICATE OF REGISTRATION

THE BRITISH APPALOOSA SOCIETY

This certificate is written evidence of the breeding of the below named animal. This acceptance is based upon application duly certified by the breeder or owner. This certificate is subject to correction and cancellation upon the Bye-laws of the British Appaloosa Society. The British Appaloosa Society will not be liable under this certificate for any mistakes therein based upon error or misrepresentation in the application thereof; and in the case of such error or misrepresentation the British Appaloosa Society reserves the right to cancel this certificate and the entry of this animal. This horse is accepted for regular registration based on photographs and certification by the applicant that this horse has sufficient colour contrast so as to be easily recognisable from 15 feet. If current photographs prove this horse to lack qualifying coat markings, the status of the registration will be changed.
The Society hereby certifies that the animal described below is recorded by the British Appaloosa Society.

Name:

Reg. No.

Sex:

Date of Birth:

Description:

Breeder:

We have hereunto affixed the seal of this Society on this date.

Date:

Secretary

Permanent papers. The Breeding (Solid Coloured) Register was for horses having Appaloosa breeding and/or in whole or part Appaloosa characteristics but not the Appaloosa coat colouring. Animals that coloured in at a later age could then be passed to the appropriate register.

As the breeding of Appaloosas is well entrenched in Britain the society now seeks to ensure that it is Appaloosas it is registering, not partbred Appaloosas. It recognizes the validity of careful outcrossing and makes provision for this by accepting these animals directly into its Foundation Register, from where the descendants of this outcross can work their way up to Stud Book status through the Grade Registers. To be eligible for these registers the horse must have a recognizable Appaloosa coat pattern, white sclera, and mottled skin.

THE FOUNDATION REGISTER is for animals with a recognizable coat pattern and required characteristics, having one registered Appaloosa parent, and for animals accepted under the Hardship clause (see below).

THE GRADE REGISTERS are for animals with a recognizable coat pattern and required characteristics and having both parents registered in the Foundation and/or Grade Registers and/or Stud Book.

Grade D   progeny of two foundation animals or one foundation animal and either a Grade D, C, B, A or Stud Book animal.

Grade C   progeny of two Grade D animals or of one Grade D and either a Grade C, B, A or Stud Book animal.

Grade B   progeny of two Grade C animals or of one Grade C and either a Grade B, A or Stud Book animal.

Grade A   progeny of two Grade B animals or of one Grade B and either a Grade A or Stud Book animal.

THE STUD BOOK is a register of the progeny of two Grade A animals, or of a Grade A animal and a Stud Book animal or of two Stud Book animals.

THE SOLID COLOUR REGISTER is for animals, excluding stallions, having registered Appaloosa breeding (both parents) but having no easily recognizable coat pattern. If at a later date an animal develops an easily recognizable coat pattern and the required characteristics, it may be transferred, on application to the Secretary, into the appropriate Register or the Stud Book. Unless the animal colours out it will be classified as having foundation status for breeding purposes. Solid colour animals are not eligible to enter Appaloosa shows or exhibitions, but are eligible for the Appaloosa Performance Competition (in other words they must gain their points in open competition).

THE RECORD OF IDENTIFIED BREEDING is a registered list of animals, excluding stallions, having only one registered Appaloosa parent but having no easily recognizable coat pattern. Such a horse will not be registered as an Appaloosa, but be issued with a certificate of pedigree as proof of breeding. If at a later date it develops a coat pattern and required characteristics it may be transferred, on application to the Secretary, into the Foundation Register. Horses on the ID register do not count as registered Appaloosas, and so are not eligible to enter Appaloosa shows or exhibitions, nor the Appaloosa Performance Competition.

Stallions, which must have a recognizable coat pattern and required characteristics, will not be entered into the Registers or Stud Book unless they hold a BApS or MAFF veterinary licence issued in accordance with the society's regulations. The society requires a BApS licence for stallions as soon as they are two years old. This licence is issued after veterinary examination to ensure that the colt is free from hereditary defects such as parrot mouth, cryptorchidism or monorchidism, and is sound in wind and limb. If they are not licensed they must be gelded or their papers will be cancelled. On obtaining a licence they will be transferred from the Colt register, where they are originally entered, to the appropriate Register/Stud Book, provided they are 14 hands or over at two years old, to be measured not later than 31 March of that year. If gelded they will be registered appropriately.

All registered animals are issued a permanent number which will be preceded by a letter or letters denoting the Register. Thus FR = Foundation Register; G = Grade followed by the appropriate letter; SC denotes Solid Colour, SB denotes Stud Book. M stands for mare, S for stallion, G for gelding and C for colt. To illustrate by a well-known example, the stallion Rodega Tobias is registered as GD/S/430.

Imported horses which are registered with an approved Appaloosa society and show the appropriate colour may be registered in accordance with the formula laid down for the Foundation and Grade Registers. Solid coloured animals may be registered in accordance with either the Solid Colour Register or the Identified Breeding Record as appropriate.

The hardship clause covers the occasional Appaloosa of unknown or unregistered

Rodega Tobias is BApS registration number GD/S/430, indicating that he is a stallion in Grade D.

Appaloosa breeding that may be superior to the average of the breed. A special application for registration is required entailing detailed information and photographs. If deemed necessary an inspection will be made. Each application will be considered on the merits of the individual horse.

Along the path of registrations certain owners have had to relinquish papers on their animals previously thought to have been Appaloosas. This is never a decision to be taken lightly, and it has needed a single-minded attitude of the combined Council, acting in the best interests of the breed, to ensure that such decisions were taken. That such tough registration rules have been accepted, if not with equanimity but with understanding by those most affected, proves that those members had the breed's best interests at heart. It may also indicate that here the innate British conservatism has for once played a vital role. It also has a great deal to do with the level of financial involvement of most British breeders, who are nearly all what would in an international sense be considered small breeders. True, financial considerations do dictate some of a stud's policy, but never to such an extent that the financial gains outweigh the long-term good of the breed.

The conservatism of the British also dictates another factor. If a British horseowner is to be enticed into owning these excitingly coloured Appaloosas he needs to know they are well-bred horses backed by a responsible body with a well-established stud book in which the pedigree of his new acquisition can be traced. There has been a long history in Britain of antagonism amongst some of the horseowning population against common 'gypsy' horses, many of which are piebald, skewbald or spotted. Without meaning any disrespect to the true Romany who understands and breeds first-class horseflesh, the epithet all too often conjures up a picture of gross, carthorse-like equines, complete with poor heads, upright shoulders, and atrocious hooves heavily befeathered, combined with undesirable high action.

That this uncompromising line on registration has been taken is largely due to the ideals of constantly upgrading the British stock that were accepted and practised by the catalyst for the Appaloosa breed in Britain, the Rivaz Stud.

Australia

The Australian Appaloosa Association Ltd (AAA) differs in several respects from those of the USA and Britain. All Australian Appaloosas must reach a minimum of 14 hands by four years of age, and according to classification they fall into one of three main divisions. As with other registries the four identifiable characteristics are the same: coat pattern, mottled skin, striped hooves and white sclera. Horses eligible for registry must have one parent registered with the AAA, and the other either with the AAA or with one of the approved registries. These are: Australian Jockey Club Registered Thoroughbreds; Australian Stud Book; Australian Quarter Horse Association; Australian Stock Horse Society; Arabian Horse Society of Australia; German Warm Blood Society.

Artificial insemination is permitted, but semen may only be used at the same location where the stallion is standing at stud. No more than fifty mares per year may be bred by AI from any one stallion. Only 500 straws of semen may be used after a stallion's death. None may be used after a stallion is gelded, except in special circumstances adjudicated by the AAA Board of Directors.

All foals must be branded, either by freeze brand or fire, with the owner's mark and the reference number and last number of the year of foaling. Foals will not be accepted for registration unless branded. Any registered Appaloosa found to be unbranded will have its papers rescinded until it is branded.

All colts must be progeny recorded within their first twelve months. Coloured colts are identified by a 'PC' number, and solid coloured colts by a 'P' number. At two years of age colts must be inspected by a veterinary surgeon and meet certain criteria before passing to the Adult Register. This veterinary inspection ensures that no monorchid or cryptorchid colts are admitted as stallions. In addition both testes must be of equal size. Colts with parrot mouths or undershot jaws are also barred, as are any with visible signs of hereditary unsoundness. At the time of the veterinary examination colts must measure a minimum of 14 hands. Progeny sired by a monorchid or cryptorchid, which could be possible when using an outcross stallion, is also ineligible for registration unless it is gelded or spayed. Once passed the colt enters either the Adult or the Breeding Stock Register, as described below.

All coloured fillies are eligible to enter the Adult Register at birth, provided they are neither parrot mouthed nor have undershot jaws. All Adult Register horses must also exhibit white sclera. The Breeding Stock Register is for Appaloosa-bred horses that do not exhibit a coloured coat pattern. They may have other Appaloosa characteristics but must have a white sclera. If they colour out later they are advanced to the Adult Register. The Appaloosa Bred Registry is for stock that have the breeding but lack any characteristics. Their progeny can only be accepted into the Progeny, Adult, Breeding Stock or Gelding Registries if they are bred to an Adult or Breeding Stock registered horse. If a Breeding Stock Appaloosa is registered in the Palomino or Buckskin Registry and subsequently colours out and the owner wishes to advance the horse to Adult Register status, the colour breed papers must be surrendered. A horse that loses its colour will have its papers recalled and returned stamped 'not eligible to be shown, raced or exhibited as an Appaloosa'. If it is a stallion the Council has the discretion to decide whether he shall remain eligible to stand at stud.

The AAA also operates a hardship clause whereby a horse that may not have the required pedigree but is nevertheless a superior Appaloosa may be registered. The format for registering such a horse is similar to that operated by the BApS.

Imported horses are accepted into the AAA if they are already registered in the Appaloosa associations of the following countries: America, Britain, Canada, Mexico and New Zealand. All imported stallions must also be classified (veterinary inspected) before registration in the AAA.

Canada

The Appaloosa Horse Club of Canada is an association incorporated under the

CERTIFICATE OF PEDIGREE

The Appaloosa Horse Club Of Canada

Incorporated Under The Livestock Pedigree Act · 1961 (Canada Dept. of Agriculture) Ottawa, Canada

THIS CERTIFICATE is written evidence of the breeding of the below named animal. **Subject to the provisions and bylaws of The Appaloosa Horse Club of Canada now in force, the club hereby certifies that the Appaloosa**

	NAME
Stallion	Silver Cloud Kestral
SEX	

is recorded by The Appaloosa Horse Club of Canada, and that the recorded number is   9073

COLOUR and DESCRIPTION   Light Chestnut:frosting over back & rump,chestnut spots, mottled muzzle,star,snip, R hind coronet.Bred:Col.V.D.S.Williams, Bucks,England.Owned:Mrs.W.Pellant,Willingston Farm Stud, Moreton Hampstead, Devon,England

PEDIGREE : FOALED March 19,1972

SIRE	Sunrise Speckled Hawk #2426 ApHCC	Domino Speckled Prince # 1807 ApHCC
		Shiela #F2259 USA
DAM	Jaguar's Kandy K # 3383 ApHCC	Morgans Jauary #9008 USA
		Squalicum Dreamer #2994 USA

IN WITNESS WHEREOF:
We have hereunto affixed the seal of this Assn., at Calgary,Alberta., Date April 2,1975

_____
PRESIDENT

_____
SECRETARY

Registration certificate of Silver Cloud Kestral with the Appaloosa Horse Club of Canada. Compare pp. 85 and 93 to see how the original colour of the horse has lightened.

Livestock Pedigree Act of the Government of Canada. The ApHCC has two sections to its registry: the Book of Registry and the Book of Record. The former is for animals qualified in all respects as Appaloosas, the latter for animals lacking any colour or insufficient colour and/or Appaloosa characteristics, but which are of Appaloosa breeding. These may be used for breeding but are not eligible to show in Appaloosa classes. All horses in the Canadian registry must be inspected prior to acceptance. One parent must be registered or recorded with the ApHCC or the ApHC. The other parent can be from the following:

> The ApHCC Book of Registry or Book of Record
> The ApHC, Moscow, Idaho, USA: Foundation, Permanent, Tentative or Breeding Stock only, although some Pedigree Certificate horses may be acceptable if they meet the requirements of the ApHCC
> The AQHA: numbered and Appendix registered horses
> The Jockey Club (Thoroughbred) of New York
> The Canadian Thoroughbred Horse Society, Canadian National Livestock Records, Ottawa, Ontario
> The Canadian Quarter Horse Association, Canadian National Livestock Records, Ottawa, Ontario.

Additionally animals must meet conformational and other requirements – such as a lack of pony blood – similar to those regulations in other countries. However, the Canadians are more specific and somewhat stricter over the parrot mouth condition, and exceed even the strict Australian rules on monorchid and cryptorchid stallions, bars to registration extending to perfect foals from monorchid or cryptorchid stallions, so that outcross stallions and their get of breeds otherwise acceptable are not registerable.

Although American-registered Appaloosas are eligible for Canadian registration they must *also* meet with full Canadian rules and be inspected prior to acceptance into either of the Canadian registries. This would exclude horses who lack colour and Appaloosa characteristics from the full registry, neither would they be eligible to compete in Canadian Appaloosa show classes.

America

The ApHC requirements for a horse to be accepted into its Registry are somewhat

First Draft, an American born and registered Appaloosa, across country with current owner Jim Dobson.

different to those current in the BApS, ApHCC and the AAA. Just as certain types of registration certificate are being phased out in the British Registry to bring all horses within the grading scheme towards ultimate Stud Book status, certain elements in the American system are also becoming obsolete. Horses registered prior to 1 January 1983 will be in possession of old forms and in some cases can apply for re-classification.

The basic registration system of the ApHC is listed below.

All horses shall measure 14 hh by five years of age.
A horse with a parrot mouth or an undershot jaw is ineligible for registration unless gelded or spayed.
Horses with pony, draught, pinto, albino or paint blood are ineligible.
All horses must be of riding type with desirable conformation.
The ApHC reserves the right to examine horses prior to registration or re-classification of papers.

The minimum requirements for obtaining Regular papers are that the horse must have a recognizable Appaloosa coat pattern or mottled skin and one other characteristic – either a white sclera or striped hooves. One parent must be registered with the ApHC. The other parent must be registered with the ApHC or one of the approved breed associations. These are the American Quarter Horse Association, the Jockey Club of New York, or the Arabian Horse Club Registry of America. As the rule book stands at present use of a Thoroughbred or an Arabian registered in any other country's official stud book will bar entry to the ApHC Registry.

Appaloosa mares and stallions that are registered under any of the following categories must be bred to an Appaloosa with Regular papers to validate their progeny's registry.

No Characteristics (N/C): although of Appaloosa breeding the horse does not show any Appaloosa characteristics whatsoever.
Breeding Stock Only (BSO): exhibiting characteristics other than coat colour.
Breeding Stock, No Characteristics (BSN): the same as N/C, but this category is being phased out.
Certified Pedigree Option (CPO): see below.
Identification Papers (ID)
Pedigree Certificate (PC)

ID and PC papers cover horses of non-Appaloosa blood that are used in an Appaloosa breeding programme. They may also cover Appaloosa horses with no characteristics.

As from 1 January 1983, all horses in the Regular Registry were also entered in the Permanent Registry. Prior to that date there were Tentative and Permanent Registries. Tentative papers denoted horses either with an unknown pedigree; or out of unregistered Appaloosa stock; or with one parent registered with any of the acceptable breed associations; or with Tentative registered parents. To acquire Permanent papers a stallion had to sire twelve foals eligible for the Regular Registry. A mare had to produce three foals so eligible. Horses foaled prior to 1 January 1983 that exhibit characteristics but no coat colour are eligible towards the count, but non-characteristic animals are not. Once a horse is Permanent registered its offspring can advance to Permanent if they meet all registration requirements. Tentative stallions later gelded and Tentative mares later spayed can also enter the Permanent Registry if they meet other registration requirements.

The introduction of the CPO (Certified Pedigree Option) scheme has caused much controversy. To be eligible for this the horse must be registered with the ApHC and be inspected by a ApHC designee. It is aimed at establishing that horses not exhibiting Appaloosa characteristics are in fact the progeny of the stated parents, which must be horses whose breeding is acceptable to the ApHC as eligible for registration in the Regular Registry. Prior to the inception of this programme on 1 January 1983, horses registered as Non-Characteristic, Breeding Stock, and Breeding Stock with No Characteristics were ineligible to compete in any Appaloosa events. Now any horse who passes through the CPO scheme is awarded papers with the prefix CN before the registration number, and is entitled to participate in all approved ApHC events against recognizable Appaloosas. This is the main cause of aggravation. Should a CN horse later develop Appaloosa characteristics he may be passed to the Regular Registry.

As the registration rules now stand a CPO, N/C or BSN horse used for breeding must be bred to a horse with Regular papers. However, that horse may itself be the result of a cross between Appaloosa and Thoroughbred, Quarter Horse or Arabian. If the progeny carries colour or mottled skin and one other characteristic it goes into the Regular Registry. This horse can in turn be outcrossed yet again to another Non-Characteristic horse, and provided the colour and characteristic genes keep performing well the resulting progeny carries Regular papers. If not, it is entitled to go into the CPO programme. It does not take too much applied mathematics to figure out that eventually these Appaloosas will have virtually no Appaloosa blood in them to speak of. What it can do eventually, and not too eventually at that, is to prove just how strong colour and characteristic genes are. It could also result in more CPO horses in the Registry than Regular horses, if it goes on *ad infinitum*.

The only bar to the CPO programme, which is voluntary, is the considerable expense of proving parentage of the applicant. Any breeder or owner wishing to enter a horse into this scheme has a long road ahead of him, punctuated by hefty veterinary and laboratory bills. The horse in question and his sire and dam must all be blood typed and the results recorded with the ApHC. Additionally an ApHC inspector has to attend to identify the horse being blood typed. All his expenses must be met. At the time the blood is taken all animals in the scheme under one year of age must either be freeze marked, or identified by trichoglyphs by the inspector. Older horses must be tattooed by the inspector or freeze marked. If the horse for which application is being made, his sire and dam are all at one location the expense would obviously be considerably less than if all three animals are at different locations.

That this ruling has come into force suggests that the fiscal rewards of breeding, showing and training have dominated recent politics. Earlier, when non-characteristic Appaloosas were barred from competition, this was accepted as one of the gambles in the breeding game. It was also an inducement to use lines that were strong colour producers, albeit still with the element of chance involved. The American Quarter Horse Association takes a strong line with Appaloosa outcrops occurring in its breed. Although these are progeny of registered Quarter Horses papers are not issued to outcrops. Sometimes an inflexible rule works to a breed's advantage, even though temporary setbacks to a breeder may occur. The current relaxation by the ApHC permits too great a dilution of Appaloosa blood, and prevents fixing any specific type, unless partbreds of the three named outcross breeds are aimed at. It could indeed be used to personal advantage by those more interested in material gain and showring acclaim than in the best interests of a breed which so many have worked to re-establish for its early positive qualities.

The ruling over permitted outcrosses also creates several anomalies. While appreciating that it is a national registry's prerogative to draw up its own set of registration rules, the rules regarding outcrossing seem illogical. In the first place, even should the already registered Appaloosa be of 100 per cent Appaloosa blood, which is just about impossible going from the records, the offspring would only contain 50 per cent of such blood. Again from the same premise that it is possible for an Appaloosa to have 100 per cent Appaloosa blood, it could well be that horses with 75 per cent or more of Appaloosa blood would be denied registry with the ApHC merely because the other percentage was not registered with any of the other named registries. It seems doubly illogical that two of the three breeds permitted as an outcross must be American. This is understandable in the case of the Quarter Horse because this is clearly a breed that is 100 per cent American, although its history also shows that much outside blood has been used, especially recently. But the terms 'American Thoroughbred' and 'American Arabian' defy logic. An Arabian is an Arabian whatever country it is registered in, providing the registry is a member of WAHO (the World Arab Horse Organization). The Arabian Horse Club Registry of America accepts for example British and Polish Arabians into its registry. Britain accepts American Arabians into the Arab Horse Society. A similar situation exists in the American Jockey Club. Many Thoroughbred mares of American breeding cross to England to be covered by English Thoroughbred stallions and vice versa, and the resulting progeny are accepted into the Jockey Club or Weatherbys. The Thoroughbred racing scene is truly international, with an interchange of Thoroughbred racing on many European tracks as well as those in America. Why then does the ApHC stipulate that an outcross must be to an American registered Arabian or Thoroughbred, when those same registries also accept horses of the same breed foaled in a different country and registered in that country's appropriate registry?

If such outcrosses are to continue to be permitted why not take a leaf out of the rule book of the American Quarter Horse Association and accept Jockey Club registered horses as well as Thoroughbreds registered in the stud book appropriate to their country of origin and domicile? Indeed it could happen that a Quarter Horse upgraded from the Appendix to the numbered register carries the Thoroughbred side of his blood from one of the foreign registries for Thoroughbreds that the ApHC denies recognition to.

With the international trade in horses increasing, and with Appaloosa breeders still seeking ApHC registration for their British-bred horses, should they wish to use either an Arabian or a Thoroughbred outcross they must seek the very rare horse that is also imported from America because British Arabians or Thoroughbreds are not acceptable. This is not a problem with European Quarter Horses as they are normally registered in America.

Considerations on breed status

So where does this lead us? Several countries have their own very distinctive equestrian panoramas: the Old World, essentially Europe and in particular Britain; Australia with its own vigorous horse culture that yet takes the best from Britain and America and in many cases improves on it; and the New World of the Americas with their multitudinous breeds of horse, some of which are direct imports with a worldwide registry, and others which have become known as American breeds.

Much of the foundation blood of the latter was stock that had been 'acclimatized' to North America and then set on the road to breed status by importations of horses largely from Britain and Europe. Amongst these American breeds are the American Quarter Horse, the Morgan, the Saddlebred, the Standardbred, and the Appaloosa.

Correction, not the Appaloosa.

Although the ApHC may claim to be the international registry for Appaloosas, accepting registrations from abroad and listing other national societies as 'foreign affiliates', it should more correctly be the International Registry for the American Appaloosa – for horses admitted to the American Registry. Other horses just as entitled, and in many cases more so, to the breed nomenclature are denied recognition by this 'international' association, and here lies another illogicality. The ApHC has in the past been proud to admit that historically the ancestors of the Appaloosa breed in America stemmed from horses brought in by the Conquistadores. It is only common sense to expect that descendants of these horses were to be found along the entire route of eventual horse movements in the North American continent. It was when the Nez Percé started selectively breeding for the traits that were, up to a few years ago, truly valued as Appaloosa characteristics that the major step was taken towards breed status (with type and characteristics fixed).

A parallel situation arose in Europe. Even before the time of the Conquistadores, and for centuries thereafter, Spain provided many horses, both spotted and solid coloured, to royal courts and private studs throughout Europe. Much the same must be said for the Knabstrup, which categorically states that its foundation mare was Spanish and spotted.

So here we have the roots diverging, as roots will, but all stemming from the same tap root.

Confusion arises when the term 'breed' becomes virtually interchangeable with 'register'. They are two totally different things. The former is the result of selective breeding for generations until a certain stamp of animal capable of reproducing the same fixed type emerges. A registry is a record of animals which conform to regulations devised by a body of people who choose either to accept or deny entry to that registry. A 'breed registry' is one wherein animals are registered that conform to the characteristics and fixed type of the evolved breed, and which does not admit blood of a different breed. Along the road to achieving a breed registry, however, such outside blood is acceptable and frequently necessary. Certain breeds in America were created this way. Even the Arabian in his very earliest beginnings a thousand and more years ago was also subject to this law. The English Thoroughbred of much more recent breed status has also followed this path. Yet today it is not permitted to infuse any outside blood whatsoever into these two dominant breeds and still consider the results as Arabians or Thoroughbreds. The progeny of any outcrossing becomes a partbred of the breed – an Anglo-Arab, a partbred Arabian, or a part Thoroughbred.

In America, when the original Nez Percé horses were debased by infusions of draught blood, the pure-blooded horses left were too few to maintain pure status without close inbreeding. In any case the political climate did not permit quality horsebreeding amongst the Nez Percé. Consequently when the time came to upgrade the Appaloosa once again, the coarse blood had to be bred out by excessive dilution.

A useful first-cross Appaloosa, Tibertich Destiny by the Thoroughbred stallion Hyrossi out of an Appaloosa mare. Ridden by Lucia Boase.

In Europe too the quality Spanish blood was, over the centuries, debased until most spotted horses, both those with Appaloosa characteristics and colouring and the ordinary spotted horses, became heavily infused with 'carty' blood.

Steps were taken in Britain and in other European countries to upgrade the spotted horses. Britain in particular had a strong market, with many of her Appaloosa horses going to other European countries as well as Australia. She in turn used a certain amount of American Appaloosa blood, and horses of essentially English blood were accepted into the American registry.

However, there is a divergence in type of horse according to country of origin and this is mainly because breeders breed the type, still within the breed framework, that will suit the nationality to which they cater. Hence in America by far the largest percentage of Appaloosas are Western orientated with a stockier frame, heavier muscling, and overall lower height range, while the most desirable in Britain are of hunter stamp, with longer, leaner muscling, and a somewhat higher height range.

There are of course many exceptions. The British Tibertich stud breed more for the Western stamp of horse, as do Amazing Appaloosas, and in America the reverse occurs where hunter/jumper people favour the English type.

Breed status aside, there is the matter of colour in Appaloosas. Each registry has its own set of regulations over solid-colour horses. The crucial question is whether the Appaloosa is a *breed* or a *colour breed*. Is it a breed with traceable and non-diffuse bloodlines for enough generations to warrant a stud book of purebred animals? Or is it a colour breed, where providing a horse has the colour and some characteristics it is registerable in the breed registry even though the percentage of Appaloosa blood is minimal? And what of the situation where no Appaloosa colour or characteristics are needed, and precious little Appaloosa blood either, yet horses can still be considered registerable?

Once stud book status is reached outcrossing, no matter how the title of the resulting progeny is packaged, results in a partbred. As such it will take generations of intensifying with unadulterated Appaloosa blood to work the way back to stud book status and purebred Appaloosas.

Working towards raising any purebred horse is a lengthy process. For those fortunate enough to purchase all their foundation stock with requisite pedigree some savings can be made on the way towards the ultimate goal of possessing purebred stock, or as purebred as is possible with a breed that is only a few decades old in its modern form. Relaxing registry rules is not the way to solve problems. The resultant horses may be beautiful animals in their own rights – a part Arabian, part Appaloosa can be a truly beautiful horse with all the refinement of the Arabian, the dual hardiness and endurance of both breeds, and the colour inheritance of the Appaloosa – but it is a part Appaloosa or part Arabian however you look at it. The same goes for infusions of Quarter Horse or Thoroughbred blood. If the Appaloosa is to be considered a breed by blood, these principles hold true.

Appaloosa societies in all countries permit outcrosses. The differences lie in the way each society sees the value of its registry. In Britain the progeny of an outcross goes back to square one of Foundation Registry, and it takes the requisite five generations of 'pure' breeding to work back to Stud Book status, hoping that the desired qualities that justified such an outcross have been fixed. It may be of interest to note here that at the time of writing horses imported directly from America with full ApHC registration can only achieve at best a Grade C classification in the British Registry, and their offspring have to work their way to full Stud Book status. One solution that could be considered for the ApHC is recognition of a Part-Bred

Register carrying with it full performance rights, with halter (in-hand) horses being shown in their separate divisions. This would obviate the feeling of unfairness engendered when breeders who have striven to breed 'pure' Appaloosas have to show against horses who are the results of continual outcrossing. It is undeniable that in Britain, for instance, some partbreds (especially amongst the Quarter Horse breed which has a registry for these animals) are in fact superior animals to their purebred brethren. These cases are always the result of using a superior stallion and a superior mare from the two breeds that make up the package of the partbred progeny.

6 Requirements of the Appaloosa in Britain

Financial considerations

As a British publication naturally concerned with the British side of the Appaloosa breed, this book deals with several aspects of Appaloosa ownership that differ greatly from those concerning these horses in, if not their country of origin, their twentieth-century pivotal base in America.

Finance governs these differences more than any other factor. Other points that go to make up the national breed package are the expectancies of the majority of individual owners and the relative non-monetary values of certain aspects of the horse: its prime conformation requirements; the way a British judge views the show animal; the animal's own imposed lifestyle, which for a horse on the British show circuit is drastically different from its American counterpart; the performance normally expected of the average British horse.

Before I cover the financial 'hot potato' I can hear readers say: 'but it costs a fortune to raise and keep a horse in any location, regardless of which side of the Atlantic it is on'. Granted there are many amongst all levels of horseowners, whatever their breed preference, who find it a struggle to maintain their individual horse or small nucleus of breeding stock.

In Britain the Appaloosa is a relatively new breed in the collective sense, even though individual specimens have been found over many centuries. Most British studs consist of a small band of broodmares and youngstock, sometimes without a resident stallion. Even the larger studs send their mares out to be covered by the stallion of their choice. Some studs stand one stallion, a few two, and the very rare operation might have three entires at stud. The acreage over which these stud farms operates is also very limited, ranging from the very smallest operation with less than 10 acres, to what we term a large stud of several hundred acres. These 'hundreds of acres', however, are in reality not for the horse side of the operation which is usually, even in the most professional of equestrian circles, carried on as an adjunct to the main operation of farming. Stud fees obtainable for even the very best of breed are exceptionally low when compared with their US counterparts, ranging from £100 to a maximum of £250, and the price range for top quality youngstock is also much lower, as are the prices obtainable for mature animals. There are of course exceptions, particularly should an Appaloosa become successful in show jumping. In the early days of the British Appaloosa Society a visiting American breeder commented on how low the prices were for stock that in the USA would have fetched a very much higher price. Raising and maintaining these animals, on the other hand, is not at such a favourable ratio and a recent enquiry confirmed that the nuts and bolts of day-to-day management – feed, hay, farriery, veterinary care and long-term saddlery purchases – show little difference in price between the two countries.

Climatic considerations also enter into the finance. Britain, and much of Europe too, has the type of climate that often necessitates horses wintering in. In particular lack of sufficient pasturage means heavy poaching and grass root destruction in wet weather, in addition to loss of condition in the stock. We do have superb pasture in summer months, sometimes too rich for the good of the horse's hooves, which may also necessitate keeping horses in for a great deal of the time. This all adds to the cost. But what effect does this have on owner requirements? The average British owner,

The versatile Appaloosa in open competition: Klaus cross country.

and this includes those that exhibit at the major show that would equate with Class A shows in the USA, therefore demands a very versatile animal that is also extremely tough. In Britain we generally do not consider an animal very versatile if he can only compete in a variety of show classes held at, hopefully, ideal venues. The British Appaloosa must also expect to be hunted, hunter trialled, show jumped, ridden in both competitive trail and endurance rides, and in the height of the show season carry his rider in both the English ridden and occasionally the Western events around the country. The average British rider is usually 'jump crazy', so the average Appaloosa, not just the specialist horse, is very adept over natural and coloured fences.

Judging aspects

Owners also expect to campaign their horses against other breeds in open classes, as their horses' chances to compete against their peers in events restricted to members

The versatile Appaloosa: Klaus at a charity dressage function with rider in eighteenth-century dress.

of the Appaloosa breed are relatively few. It is in the open shows that the real worth of these animals is being and will continue to be proved. It has been a very hard road to follow because generally speaking British horseowners have been very conservative in their choice of horses, and the most conservative of all are the experienced judges who are used to seeing the 'accepted breeds' and often can see no good reason why they should depart from the norm, even though the representative of the new breed conforms to all the class requirements. Happily this situation is beginning to change under more enlightened judges. To quote one eminent horseman and judge, Captain Elwyn Hartley Edwards, commenting on Petrukas, the Rivaz Appaloosa foundation mare: 'I could find a home for her any day.'

For these horses the prime requirement is absolute soundness. If they lack this they cannot cope with the extra stresses that hard usage imposes upon them. Added to this is the system a good British judge uses when assessing animals in the show ring. They tend to judge a horse from the hoof up, and if it does not have a good set of hooves and correct limbs all the 'breed characteristics' in the body will avail it nothing, for above all the horse must be able to perform the work for which it is bred.

In breed classes, although breed type, conformation and colour are part of the package, a British judge looks first to the underpinning. Over the past fifteen years the quality of the Appaloosas coming under scrutiny has greatly improved, largely due to judges who expect quality horses to be exhibited, and to some like Captain Hartley Edwards who have given invaluable advice to the BApS in its formative years. Unfortunately there is one class of British judge, not exclusive to Appaloosas, who insists on putting up rather coarse, heavy hunter types, lacking quality but possessing poundage. This can only be detrimental when applied to Appaloosa judging as it is extremely confusing to exhibitors who are trying to infuse quality into their horses.

In open in-hand classes, which are frequently for hunter youngstock, the judge is not only assessing the animal before him on the merits it has on that particular day, but judging whether it has the potential to make a horse suitable for the hurly burly of the hunting field and associated activities. Apart from distance riding, these equestrian occupations are where the greatest stresses will be sustained, as the terrain and ground conditions are dictated by locale, weather and soil consistency, from well-drained sandy going to the heavy plough and clayey soils that test even the toughest limbs.

For the average owner this has led to a certain type of horse being bred that is distinct from its American cousin. The average British Appaloosa does tend towards the larger type of animal, upwards of 15.2 hh and frequently with distinct hunter conformation that combines elegance, substance, good limbs and sufficient height. Of course there are the smaller Appaloosas, from 14.2 to 15.2 hh, that also fill the needs of a great many riders and who are found in just about any sphere of competition. A small percentage of these are dual purpose English and Western mounts. However, the need as opposed to the desire for a Western type of mount is not very great in Britain. Few of the Appaloosa breed are used solely in this small but growing sphere of recreational riding.

The British Appaloosa trend is therefore towards a hunter stamp of horse, which

Rodega Keziah, successful in open Western competitions, shown here after winning the Western Pleasure at the East of England Show with the author.

can if necessary, because of his equable temperament and continually improving conformation, still be used if the rider so wishes in Western competition. Currently, other than in open Western classes which are increasing, there is little outlet for the Western Appaloosa in Britain, though several horses, even up to well over 16 hands, are occasionally seen under Western tack and acquitting themselves admirably. There is also less conservatism amongst the judges in this sphere of competition.

Showing incentives

Another reason why the Appaloosa in Britain is being bred strictly with versatility in mind also hinges on finance. The major differences in top-level showing in Britain and the USA are the incentives and the approach. Huge purses can be won by good performance horses in the USA and most of the really top horses are professionally produced. In other words it costs a considerable amount to win the also considerable prize money. The opportunities for competition, albeit among the many thousands of competitors in the USA, are much more numerous than in Britain.

Most horses campaigned in Britain are owner bred or bought as youngsters, and are also owner trained and shown. Admittedly there are some Appaloosas that go to a professional for training, and I have received Appaloosas for training in this way. But, and this is a very important difference, the horses are usually sent to a professional yard to be broken and schooled, and then returned to the owner who subsequently shows them. A few horses are initially shown by their trainers, usually when the owner realizes that it is in the interests of the horse to have continuity of riding and handling in their introduction to the show ring. There is no discernible difference in successes obtained by the very good top amateurs and the professionals. The reward of showing in Britain is very largely satisfaction at having produced a good horse and trained it to a high standard. Monetary prizes barely cover the entry fee unless the horse stands first or second, and even then the take-home pay will not cover the additional cost of petrol and show venue stabling. On the face of it this may appear to describe an amateur show scene. Moneywise it is, but in performance and presentation the British show scene at its best is second to none. Obviously, as with all areas of competition, there are tail-enders and it is an unpleasant fact that it is nearly always the few who do not come up to scratch that are remembered rather than the majority who do.

There are variations in the way the British Appaloosa is expected to perform; usually in a more collected manner with better defined paces for the English classes;

73

Rivaz Limerick, one of the larger British Appaloosas, has been the mount of the whipper-in of the Quorn.

in the Western events with soft movements, but paces that are definitely discernible as the true basic ones, and with the horse creating an overall appearance that is a real pleasure to watch and, more important, giving his rider a memorable ride for all the right reasons: smoothness, responsiveness and lightness allied with an alert but calm mien. To achieve this, particularly with our very limited numbers, and to give confidence to existing Appaloosa owners and to the many who are on the verge of becoming involved with the breed, the majority of the British, call it inbred conservatism if you like, stick to the basic principles of horsemanship and refuse to be swayed by current fads.

7 Performance opportunities

Britain

In Britain the only show to be held exclusively for Appaloosas is the National Show held in late July at the National Equestrian Centre at Stoneleigh in Warwickshire. Appaloosa owners converge on Stoneleigh from all over Britain to compete in a full programme of in-hand and ridden events.

Considering the relative youth of the BApS and the difficulties of travel the members are to be congratulated for the support they give to their major event. Granted the venue is well situated with good road access in the immediate vicinity, but having travelled both the superb American routes and the British country roads to equestrian events, I can testify that the difficulties of British motoring are not in miles travelled but in the switchbacks of England's country road network. I am convinced that many of these routes were initially created by farmhorses pulling the wagon homewards from market, meandering and continually stopping to graze while the drivers slept off the effect of market day's plentiful pints.

Championship in-hand classes are the chance for prospective Appaloosa breeders and/or buyers to see a wide variety of horses of all ages and with a multitude of coat patterns. It gives mare owners the chance to compare a number of prospective sires and their progeny from different types of mares, all with the expenditure of one journey instead of the many trips that would otherwise be necessary.

In the ridden events Appaloosas have a chance to display some of the breed's vaunted versatility. The performance classes are not immutable but periodically offer new challenges to horses and riders. However, they mainly concentrate on English ridden and hunter classes with the opportunity for Western riders to show in Western Pleasure.

To date two families have been largely responsible for masterminding the annual show. For its first few years Ken and Desmie de Rivaz piloted the show, and they have been succeeded by the BApS secretaries Ann and Michael Howkins, who keep the ever-expanding event smoothly running each year. As the Appaloosa becomes more popular in Britain the BApS is planning an annual Performance Show with a much wider variety of ridden events under both English and Western tack.

The other main opportunities for Appaloosas to compete in shows solely against others of the breed are at the County and larger shows which hold sections for many different breeds, each breed having a number of exclusive classes. Current practice is to offer two in-hand classes, one for youngstock, the other for mature animals, and a Riding Horse class where horses are shown under English saddle.

Appaloosa owners are not merely claiming versatility for their horses but, probably more than with any other unusual breed in Britain, are prepared to prove it, as reference to Chapter 8 will show. Appaloosas can be found at all levels in the jumping arena, and include the mounts of well-known international show jumpers, such as Veronique Whittaker on Next Cogshall Spot On who was third in the Queen Elizabeth Cup, the major event for lady riders at the 1989 Royal International Show, and Debbie Plumley (nee Johnsey) and her sister who campaign two Appaloosas, Monterey and Sandy Toes, both sired by the American Grade A show-jumping stallion Sutter's Showboat. In the junior sphere, Linda Smart's Trooper's Artful Dodger, a 15 hand blanket Appaloosa, has a whole string of successes in open competition in Working Hunter and Hunter Trials, including championships at national level Pony Club events. He also has a very determined grip on the Small Riding Horse class at the National Show, winning it for six successive years. In cross country events Merely Diandz, a bay spotted blanket gelding, has been piloted for several seasons by Anne de Rivaz, and in the dressage arena both Klaus with Anne de Rivaz and Cockley Cley Weatherman with Brugs Nichols have been highly successful.

Although showing and competing in equestrian events is taken seriously, only a relatively few show people and a tiny percentage of horses are full-time competitors, and these are usually in the eventing, show jumping, and show hunter and hack divisions. British owners gain most of their pleasure from using their Appaloosas as all-around versatility mounts, and there are very few who would be able to devote all their time to campaigning their horses. Financial rewards, other than in racing and international level show jumping and eventing, are very small in the British horse world, and most people fit their horses around their jobs which provide the pay for the vital hay and oats.

Currently with demand outstripping the supply of quality animals, there are hundreds of Appaloosas who fill the same role as Marilyn Hollanders' mare Blythwind Skylark, who is used in just about every capacity, mostly at Riding Club level, but also successfully at County Show standard. Skylark is equally at home in an elegant Riding Horse class, over a show-jumping course, or splashing through the mud and water of a long distance ride hazard.

To encourage Appaloosa owners to campaign their horses against all comers, the

(Above)

Cockley Cley Weatherman and Brugs Nichols, aiming for the top in international dressage.

(Left)

Merely Diandz and Anne de Rivaz compete successfully in open cross country events.

Marilyn Hollanders and Blythwind Skylark crossing water on a long-distance ride.

BApS has an annual award system in which horses compete for points in both Appaloosa and open events, and the more difficult the event the greater the number of points gained. Top placing horses are awarded a premium to help offset the considerable costs of consistent campaigning.

To date, all organization of British Appaloosa events is on a voluntary basis, albeit in a professional manner. Judging also is on an honorary, expenses only, basis.

International differences

Both the British and the American show scenes owe their composition largely to the earlier uses to which riding horses were put in an era when the horse fulfilled functions far different, though related, to those he executes today.

In Britain the current show horse classes, both in-hand and ridden events, are governed largely by the uses, and their derivatives, to which the horses of the gentry were put. The eighteenth- and nineteenth-century squire's life was often dominated by a passion for fox hunting. Ladies also frequented the hunt field, riding sidesaddle. In non-hunting seasons, and in the environs of urban life, the hack took precedence. Today's show classes echo this: the hunter youngstock in-hand classes, hunter classes under saddle, riding horse, ladies' hack and sidesaddle events are all popular at British shows.

In America the scene was very different. The riding horse was hardly a luxury in the early years of American settlement. In the days when the prairie schooners trekked westwards the horse was vital as transport, and later as a means of managing the huge herds of cattle established on spreading ranches. In the Eastern states a semblance of the old English life lingered in pockets. Consequently, when the horse became a companion in leisure and the show scene started to flourish in the USA, overtones of pioneering days remained. Understandably, certain areas favour the English styles of riding and horse usage, others the Western. Some have a good balance between the two styles. Yet another style suitable for the Southern plantations arose in Saddle Seat riding. But by far the greatest percentage of early shows particularly in the Western states concentrated on the Western events, and a number followed suit in the Eastern and Southern states too. When I first started showing in North Carolina in the early 1970s an English rider was lucky to have a single English Pleasure class on offer at most shows – much the same situation pertains to the Western rider today in Britain. When I left eight years later there was a far more even mix of events, though still weighted in favour of Western contests.

America

The Appaloosa in America was initially mainly involved in Western events, though nowadays there is an increasingly strong move towards using these talented horses in English fields. The hunt fields, show-jumping arenas, and dressage competitions of the USA are getting their fair share of successful Appaloosa horses.

As the Appaloosa breed has increased numerically so too has the structure for showing expanded. Chapter 2 highlighted the basic elements of American Appaloosa competition and the full list of competitions is comprehensively covered in the Official Handbook issued annually by the ApHC. This publication is of tremendous value to competitors as it takes the guesswork out of competition. Entrants can familiarize themselves with the basic rules of each event, plus the minutiae of each class within a division. Judges are bound by the framework of the class and must judge accordingly, so theoretically at least better uniformity is gained in reaching decisions, without denying judges their personal preference, provided it is within the guidelines. A similar handbook issued by the BApS would be of inestimable value to both contestants and judges alike, particularly the former. It would also remind certain judges that they are judging Appaloosas, not heavyweight hunters. Having shown in both America and England I find the former system far more understandable, and the latter on a few occasions incomprehensible to newcomers.

Halter classes

Although the aim of both halter and in-hand classes is to find the horse with superior conformation, the American halter class is judged somewhat differently to its British counterpart.

At shows affiliated to the ApHC, each age division must be shown separately, and classes are held for weanlings, yearlings, two and three year olds of each sex. Colts and fillies are never shown in the same class. Mature horses four years and over can be shown in mixed age groups, but the sexes are divided, and a championship is awarded to each sex.

Western performance

The Western Pleasure classes form the largest group of Western performance classes. Two year olds may be shown in a snaffle bit or bosal but not until Memorial Day (late May) in their two-year-old year. Three year olds also have a snaffle bit/ bosal class allotted to them. They may, however, also show in the Junior Western Pleasure class which is open to horses four years old or under. Once a horse has been shown in a bit other than a snaffle he cannot enter the snaffle bit classes. Senior classes are for horses five years and older. (At large shows where numbers warrant, or which are run under rules which necessitate offering certain divisions, Western Pleasure classes in addition to those above will be run for ladies, men, non-professionals, youth and novice youth riders.) Horses perform at walk, jog and lope on a reasonably loose rein on both reins, and the judge may request the jog to be extended. All horses must back at the judge's request. Restrictive head equipment is prohibited, as is overly severe bitting. Cuts and abrasions by bits are grounds for elimination. Strides are to be of a reasonable length at all gaits. The jog must be ground covering and the lope at a speed that is a natural way of going. This should preclude the artificial outline and cramped gaits often seen in Western Pleasure classes, and the rule book is quite clear on its requirements for a good pleasure horse.

The Trail class is often one of the most popular events. It enables a horse to show his calmness, versatility and degree of training as he negotiates a series of obstacles. The mandatory manoeuvres are: a side pass; stepping through a series of at least four logs placed a minimum of 15 inches apart; crossing a wooden bridge; and opening, going through and closing a gate – all movements which any horse, whether he is ridden English or Western, should be able to execute with alacrity. Other obstacles are similar to those found on handy hunter courses in England, plus a few additional ones which really can show a horse's expertise – or lack of it. They include a water hazard of ditch or small pond; hobbling or ground tying the horse; carrying items from place to place; donning or removing a raincoat; backing through an L-shaped avenue of poles, a triangular set of six markers, or three markers set in a triangle or on a straight line; removing and replacing papers from a letterbox; executing a 360 degree turn within a 5 to 6 foot square. Horses must also show walk, jog and lope somewhere within the course, usually stipulated, for the judge to evaluate in combination with ability over obstacles.

The Western Riding class is designed to show a horse's training and calmness while moving at a reasonable speed. Its ten moves incorporate walk, jog and lope, crossing a log at the walk and jogging to a line of eight markers through which the horse lopes, showing a flying change of lead midway between each marker, and finishing off with a lope on a straight line up the centre, a halt and controlled backing for at least 10 feet.

Reining is often described as Western dressage. There are twelve set patterns, incorporating a varying number of circles and lead changes, the ability to move in a straight line, to rollback either to left or right without hesitation, do a sliding stop, back up over the sliding stop tracks, perform up to four and a quarter 360 degree spins, and perform pivots. Executed at controlled speed, each move is dictated by the rider, with anticipation by the horse incurring a penalty. The horse must be able to start readily in canter and maintain gait throughout unless otherwise specified.

Both Western Riding and Reining classes can be likened in some measure to dressage tests. Both have an escalating degree of difficulty. The horse is required to perform smoothly without excessive use of aids. Responsiveness of the horse helps towards a good score, whereas a sluggish or chargey horse will be penalized accordingly.

There are various Western game events, including Camas Prairie Stump Race, the Nez Percé Stake Race, and the Rope Race. The first two are run in two-horse eliminaton heats, and the Rope Race is run in groups, eliminating one horse at a time. The Stump Race is similar to a barrel race, except that two sets of markers are set up in a cloverleaf pattern opposite each other. The Stake Race is pole bending using six poles. The first horse across the common finish line goes forward to the next heat. The Rope Race is similar to musical chairs. Four-foot ropes are suspended from a line run across the arena two feet above the head of mounted riders, who must attempt to get hold of one at the signal. One rope is removed at a time until the winner is decided.

A number of cattle classes are held at ApHC shows, including Working Cow Horse, Cutting, Steer Daubing, Timed and Judged Calf Roping, and Timed and Judged Heading and Heeling. They show the Appaloosa in events in which in an earlier era he earned his oats. Working Cow Horse contests first test the horse's reining ability and subsequently work with a cow, which he must hold in position, then allow to move off down the fence turning it once each way. Finally he works it in two opposing circles. Judges make allowances if the cow is particularly recalcitrant and therefore difficult to work.

Cutting Horse classes are run in accordance with the rules of the National Cutting Horse Association. They show the horse's ability to select a calf from a herd and keep it separated. Obvious aids to the horse are penalized. Steer Daubing is a timed event, the rider aiming to put his paint mark on a designated area of the steer – a bit like picador work but without harm to the steer. In Timed Roping the roper is allowed two casts of a rope. Once roped and thrown the calf is held by the horse while the roper ties three of the calf's feet together. The maximum time allowance is 35 seconds, and the calf must remain secured for a minimum of six seconds for the run to count. Judged Roping is a test of horse and rider teamwork. The horse is judged on smoothness, speed, ropework, calfwork and manners.

Heading and Heeling is teamwork, with two riders roping a steer by head and heels in that order (the steer must be standing when roped both fore and aft). The front feet of the ropers' horses must be on the ground, and the rope dallied and tight, before the scorer calls time. Judged Heading entails the same procedure as in Heading and Heeling, but the judge assesses the heading horse only on manners and ability. The heeler is merely an adjunct. In Judged Heeling the procedure is reversed.

English performance

Performance classes under English saddle are fairly similar to classes in the British show ring. In the Hunter under Saddle class the horse is not required to jump but is judged at walk, trot and canter. The judge may ask for the trot to be extended, and for a hand gallop, although no more than eight horses may gallop at a time. Horses should back readily. Hunter under Saddle classes are held for the same categories as Western Pleasure classes. In the Hunter Hack class, the horse is worked on the flat and required to jump two fences. The main difference between Working Hunter and Green Working Hunter classes is the height of the fences, which vary from 3 foot to 3 foot 9 inches. Youth and non-professional Working Hunter classes and Equitation over Fences have heights of from 2 foot 6 inches to 3 foot with a 3 foot spread. Jumper classes are open, youth or non-professional and heights start at 3 foot 3 inches.

The only pleasure class offered under English saddle is Saddle Seat Pleasure, where horses move with more animation and collection and higher action than in hunter classes. In this class it is mandatory for the canter to be started from a walk. Sidesaddle pleasure may be ridden in either an English or a Western sidesaddle. The class may be combined, or individual classes for each type may be offered. It is the only class where a sidesaddle is permitted. The costume class invites riders and horses kitted out in costumes portraying any era of Appaloosa history such as conquistadores, Chinese emperors, kings or nobles, or in any guise recognizable from the American West. The most popular is Indian costume, which must be authentic. There are also two categories for driving horses – Buckboard Driving and English Pleasure Driving. The former may have up to two horses hitched, the latter only one.

A comprehensive number of classes are also offered to Youth and Non-Professional riders much along the above lines, but with the addition of Showmanship and Equitation for both categories, and a few extra game classes for Youth.

Distance riding

Special recognition is given to Appaloosas that are successful in long distance riding, one of the strong points of the breed where its vaunted toughness is put to the real test.

An honour system of recording saddle hours starts with chevrons for 100 and 200 hours, followed by a jump to 500 hours, and thereafter in increments of 500 up to 2,500 hours of riding.

The highest accolade in distance riding is the Chief Joseph Commemorative patch awarded for completion of 1,000 hours, ten approved Endurance and ten approved Competitive Trail Rides. Other awards for distance riding are medallions awarded on an annual basis for completion of 350 miles. Riders elect whether to ride for Endurance or Competitive Trail medallions. Endurance Rides must be a minimum of 50 miles and Competitive Trail Rides a minimum of 25 miles. Miles from both cannot be combined, but a horse can earn single or multiple medallions in one or both categories. There is also a 1,000 mile award and miles can be accumulated over an open-ended time span. Horses eligible for distance awards must be at least five years of age and registered in the appropriate registry. The riders/owners must be paid up members of the ApHC.

As a progressive society the ApHC recognizes the pleasure given to disabled riders and drivers and has started a similar system for handicapped riders and drivers where chevrons are awarded starting at the lower limit of 25 hours. A Chief Joseph Commemorative Award is given to horsemen or women who achieve 500 riding hours, and 500 driving hours plus completing five approved driving competitions. One of the most successful horses of the recent past is Dickys Chapparal, who has done sterling work in a California Riding for the Disabled Programme. He is featured in Chapter 8.

In recognition of the top horses in each category such as Racing, Halter, Performance, and Distance Riding, medallions are awarded by the ApHC each year. Bronze is awarded for achievement in one category. Two categories earn a silver, three a gold, and four a diamond medallion. Prestigious awards are available to sires and dams of gold medallion winners, the highest accolade being induction into the Appaloosa Hall of Fame when a stallion sires eight or a mare produces three progeny on the gold standard.

Canada

Canadian Appaloosa showing and performance opportunities are similar to those of the USA, with the exception of the more stringent rules covering Appaloosa colour

Silver Cloud Kestral, a British-born Appaloosa of Canadian breeding.

and characteristics for show horses. The ApHCC offers incentives in the form of annual trophies and scaled achievement awards to Youth and Amateurs. Ratings are decided on an accumulative points system for certain classes. Distance riders participating in Competitive Trail, Endurance and recreational Pleasure Riding also record their mileage and hours in the 'saddle log' programme, with appropriate chevrons and badges awarded.

Differences in showing in the UK and USA

There are a few distinct areas in which the class format differs for Appaloosas shown in Britain or the United States.

In halter or in-hand classes the first thing that is obvious is the handler's apparel. In America all handlers must be attired in Western dress. In Britain there is no stringent rule. Many wear riding clothes, boots, breeches, coat and hat, especially if they are in a performance class later. Others are in tweed jackets and casual trousers – both men and women. Ladies may show in a neat but very conservative blouse and skirt, or dress, and appropriate hat. A few show in Western attire and on one occasion this earned a Best Turned out award at the British National Appaloosa Show. The American system often gives an overall better turnout, but the insistence on Western attire for horses that subsequently show in the English divisions is rather odd – rather like stating that the Appaloosa is and will remain a Western breed in spite of the fact that many Appaloosa breeders are striving for more English riding participation.

No whips of any type are permitted in American halter classes. In British in-hand events a cane or whip is invariably carried as part of the turnout. Plaiting of manes, though not obligatory in British classes, is usual. The traditional practice with tails in Britain is to cut them square just below the hocks. They may be either pulled or plaited. When it comes to moving a horse out to show his action the British judge prefers to see the horse show a really good stride at the trot, while the American system seems content with a bit of a jog.

The ridden classes afford the greatest differences. After the initial rail work American horses will be called into a line-up, when the judge will go down the line requesting each horse to back up and making his individual inspection. He may require individual work from any horse but his choice of such work is restricted to that already performed in the work on the rail. Awards are usually then made.

In Britain the horses are called into line usually in the order of the judge's initial preference. If it is a very big ridden class there may be a front row of horses in with a hope, and a back row of tailenders. The next step is for each horse to give a brief individual performance of the rider's devising. Alternatively the judge may instruct the rider on what his solo performance is to be. The rider invariably ends his individual show with a halt and back up, then walks to his place in the line-up on a loose rein. The judge then rides each horse himself. Occasionally the back row is not ridden, but fair-minded judges always do so as just occasionally a 'sleeper' comes right up on the quality of the ride he gives the judge. The last stage is for saddles to be taken off and the judge to assess conformation.

Occasionally the judge may elect not to ride the horses, and sometimes the classes are not lined up in the order of initial preference, that being deferred until later.

There are good and bad points in both systems. The individual performances in the British system show the horse to better advantage. But a horse is trained for his owner to ride, not for what could be a great number of other individuals throughout the course of a season if the horse is shown extensively. Some judges are bound to make the owner wince over their riding ability, although fortunately some are superb riders – for example, British Appaloosas invariably go well for Mr Ramsey. The British system is far more time consuming, but exhibitors usually feel they have had their money's worth!

The jumper division also has differences, the main one being over falls of both horse and rider. In Britain these are heavily penalized and will put a horse out of the running in hunter classes, and in jumper classes a first fall earns 8 faults, and a second fall means elimination. Other than at their National Show, British Appaloosas are jumping in open competition and abide by national rules for Hunter classes and British Show Jumping Association rules for jumping events. In American Appaloosa classes falls of either or both horse and rider incur immediate elimination.

The British show scene is very cosmopolitan, and the bigger the show the greater the number of sections. Each section will cover one breed with ridden and in-hand classes. Other sections cover various activities under saddle unrelated to breed but with a definite type of horse in mind. A hunter, hack or riding horse are considered specific types. While Appaloosas, and other breeds, may enter these classes it is not often that they figure in the top line-up at the major Agricultural Shows, which is an unfortunate and blinkered attitude on the judge's part if the horses fill every other requirement. When an Appaloosa does come through it is usually in the true performance classes or events where he does more than show his paces round the ring. These tend to be eventing, show jumping, and long distance riding, where doing the job is the only thing that matters.

This highlights the biggest difference of all between the American and British Appaloosa scene. The USA has such a great number of Appaloosas that they have been able to organize a nationwide show structure of major events within the breed, and subsequently members of the breed have begun to win acceptance with

Breed promotion through open competition: Anne de Rivaz and Spot On.

increasing successes in events usually dominated by traditional breeds, such as Thoroughbreds in the English riding disciplines, Quarter Horses in the cutting and reining events, and Arabs in the long distance fields. In Britain the reverse has happened. While the BApS is steadily growing and more Appaloosa avenues are opening, the bulk of Appaloosa participation has had to be in events open to all regardless of breed. Their successes have been most valuable as breed promotion, inducing many new owners to 'go Appaloosa'.

There are also a few other differences in showing that occur in the British, American and Australian systems. In Britain it is normal to show very young horses in leather headcollars or show bridles without bits. Older horses, and stallions above yearling stage, are shown in bridles with bits. For the stallions this is sometimes a requirement, but for other in-hand classes it is left to the handler's choice. In America and Australia halter horses are never shown bitted, but in leather show halters. Australia requires a chain restraint to be used when showing Appaloosa stallions.

The age at which horses may be ridden in shows also differs. In America classes for two year olds are normal, but in Britain it is considered harmful to use a horse in any ridden sphere until he is physically mature, and British performance class rules are framed accordingly. In Britain, therefore, the only class that an Appaloosa may enter as a three year old is the Western Pleasure class. For all other classes the horse must be at least four years old.

Age also governs the category in which horses are shown. In Britain a four year old horse is entered in novice classes, but he may also enter open classes against older horses. Generally it is performance status, unless otherwise stipulated, that decides which category a horse enters, rather than age, although naturally there tends to be a younger age group in the novice sections. In America a 'junior horse' is four years of age and younger. In Australia junior horses are five years of age and younger. After these ages they are considered senior horses: American Appaloosas from five onwards, Australian from six years of age upwards.

When the term 'junior' or 'senior' is used in America, Canada and Australia it always refers to the horse's age, while a child is referred to as 'youth'. In Britain, 'junior' denotes a child rider, and 'youngstock' a young horse.

Australia

The Australian show scene offers a variety of events to Appaloosa owners in both the English and Western arena, and takes something from both the Old Country and the New World. With the exception of halter and Indian costume classes which are run under AAA rules, all other performance events are governed by the rules of the Horse Show Association of Australia.

For competition purposes a horse is to be aged by the state of tooth eruption. The guide for determining this is according to that adopted by the Australian Veterinarians' Association. No horse is permitted to show in Appaloosa classes unless he exhibits an Appaloosa coat pattern. Where two horses tie on merit the horse most obviously an Appaloosa will stand highest.

Halter classes have a stipulated percentage allotment of 40 per cent for conformation and 20 per cent each for suitability, soundness and action. No whips are permitted and stallions must be shown in a halter with chain restraint. Bridles with bits are not permitted in any halter classes. Exhibitors may be dressed in either English or Western attire.

The major events recognized by the AAA in order of prestige are: the National Appaloosa Show; State Championship Shows; Class A, Class B, and Recognized Shows. Under the last title come Agricultural and Annual Horse Shows and Pony Club Annual Open Gymkhanas, as well as shows run by individuals or organizations that have AAA approval for the events. Also included are events run by any recognized EFI or EFA affiliated body. The National and State categories hold a full range of breed classes, and to qualify as Class A or B, shows must hold a minimum number of classes, including ten halter classes and a set number of performance and showmanship events depending on the class of show. At recognized shows with Appaloosa classes the choice of events is governed by the show's individual organizers.

The AAA runs a points system with a graded table of points allocated according to the number of entries in the class and the placing obtained by the competitor's horse. There are Annual High Point Awards for horses and riders competing in almost every discipline. Pony Club riders can accrue points from Official Pony Club Gymkhanas, but to prevent 'pot hunting' only the best fifteen showings count towards the award.

Dressage and eventing are also recognized in the awards system, and in these spheres as well as show jumping Australian Appaloosas are making big strides. One of the best-known eventing horses is Jim and Ruth Roberts' Bush Artist, who had a spectacular rise through the Restricted Novice section to end up winning the Novice One Day Event National Championships in 1988. Encouraged by this, the Roberts entered him in the novice section of his first Three Day Event at Gawler, where he came second. Upgrading to Intermediate as a result of his Gawler success, and constantly winning or placing in the first three, he was named the Equestrian Federation of Australia's South Australian Event Horse of the Year. Another Appaloosa shooting through the eventing ranks is Peppercorn Farms' Prince William

Mop, who is partnered by Heath Ryan, an Australian representative three-day event rider who considers the stallion to have international eventing prospects and capabilities.

The structured system of Appaloosa awards, again based on the points system, starts with an Encouragement Award followed by the Recognition Award, Register of Merit, and the bronze, silver and gold medallion series. The two highest awards are the AAA Champion Certificate and the Superior All Round Horse. Qualifications for the Champion Certificate are a minimum of 160 points, a Register of Merit at halter, and three Registers of Merit in performance. Superior Horse Award requirements are 100 points at halter, 100 points in one of the recognized performance events, and at least four Registers of Merit in performance.

8 Appaloosa portraits

The following selection of Appaloosa portraits is the author's choice. Some have been chosen because they were trailblazers for the British Appaloosa. Certain Appaloosas, while not generally known to British readers, nevertheless had and have a continuing influence on the breed. Others just could not be ignored, nor would I have wished to do so, because their current successes herald their future impact. Others I must admit to including because of the impression individual studs and horses made on me as a horsewoman and writer. For all that, no book could include the legion of Appaloosas that make up the solid base on which a breed is founded and flourishes.

Some information I gleaned from BApS literature; much was furnished by owners who either wrote to me at length, or whom I visited on fact-finding searches; the balance comes from personal observation over the years at equestrian events.

These cameos are just a glimpse which I hope will entice horsemen and horsewomen to expand their acquaintance with a breed that is now well entrenched in Britain; that owes much to many dedicated British studs; and which in the cases of some British breeders also owes a lot to the American studs which are still raising the old-time Appaloosa that Claude Thompson and Dr Francis Haines would have approved of. There is a small but steady stream of Appaloosas crossing the Atlantic to Britain's shores. The qualities they are able to impart represent the prized traits of a dual European and American heritage.

Silver Cloud Appaloosas

The late Colonel V. D. S. Williams' estate at East Burnham Park in Buckingham-shire was home to the first stud in England of registered Appaloosas (in this case registered in Canada). Though small in numbers the stock was of the highest quality, as was to be expected of such a renowned equestrian centre where Colonel and Mrs Williams were well known for producing international dressage and event horses.

The four Appaloosas were all of Canadian origin, and some were double registered with the ApHC. The stallion Sunrise Speckled Hawk, foaled in 1965, was by the Canadian Grand Champion Domino Speckled Prince out of Sheila. He arrived in England in 1966 as a gift from Walter Hughes of the Sunrise Ranch in British Columbia, and was shortly followed by the three mares Jaguar's Kandy K,

Emerald Mist and War Dance Whoopee, the latter two having achieved championship status in Canada and America. Two were in foal and their fillies helped swell the stud's numbers, and to these were added their later progeny by Sunrise Speckled Hawk, most of which were fillies – a breeder's dream.

Shortly after Sunrise Speckled Hawk was broken to saddle he appeared at the 1971 Royal International Horseshow at Wembley, where he gave a demonstration of basic training, the highlight of which was the rapport between the stallion and his rider. He was also ridden and jumped without a bridle. This was a remarkable feat for a horse new to ridden work, let alone an exhibition, as the atmosphere in the Wembley Arena is highly charged (as I can attest, having ridden my own Arabian stallion there in a Parade of Champions).

Sadly for the soon to emerge Appaloosa Society in Britain, Sunrise Speckled Hawk died as the result of a tragic road accident less than a week after showing packed Wembley audiences just what an Appaloosa could do if given the advantage of first-class training.

It was to be a number of years before Appaloosa versatility was to be shown to such advantage again, and when it was it was largely due to the talents of the Rivaz Stud horses, amongst whom was a daughter of Sunrise Speckled Hawk and their foundation mare Petrukas, the filly Rivaz Burletta.

The blood of Silver Cloud Appaloosas is now distributed throughout many of the studs in Great Britain, and the spear side is carried on mainly through the blood of Silver Cloud Kestral, by Sunrise Speckled Hawk out of Jaguar's Kandy K. He is

Silver Cloud Kestral, by Sunrise Speckled Hawk out of Jaguar's Kandy K, bred by Col. V. D. S. Williams, owned by John Luckett and leased to Amazing Appaloosas.

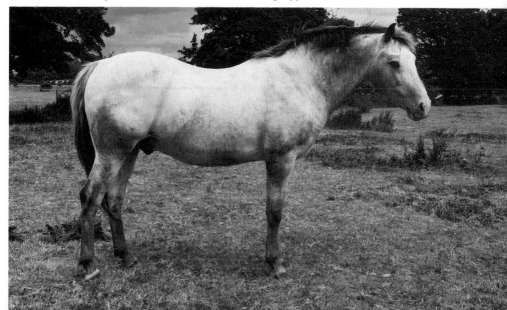

owned by John and Mary Luckett of Durcombe Water in Lynton, Devon, but has been leased to Amazing Appaloosas. He has carried on the tradition of Appaloosa amenability and toughness, being regularly hunted, and also being one of the first Appaloosas to hit the distance trail in Britain. John Luckett says that Kestral is an excellent colour producer, particularly of blanket foals. One of his mares, Wrekin Japonica, has produced a series of foals of which the Lucketts have retained five. No two have the same base colour, but all have a white blanket. Kestral himself is a light chestnut with frosting over back and rump, with chestnut spots.

The Rivaz Stud

The Rivaz Stud was briefly mentioned in connection with the start of the BApS registry and the foundation mare Petrukas. Important as mare power is, the horse that personifies the stud is undoubtedly Klaus (1973), a brown spot leopard of 16

Rivaz Stud's prolific winner Klaus, a leopard stallion by Golden Cape (TB) out of Musse, now owned by Anne de Rivaz.

hands, by Golden Cape (TB) ex Musse (Netherlands Appaloosa Registry). Already successful as a sire and show horse in Holland, he has set a record that will surely remain unequalled in any breed, winning the National Male Championship no less than ten times. In 1987 he was retired from in-hand showing but still competes under saddle. He has accrued a variety of awards and trophies from Riding Horse classes to Working Hunter at shows, and in the wider field of stressful performance as a dressage horse and hunter, generally partnered by Anne de Rivaz. In dressage he competed at Intermediate level and has accumulated a lifetime score in excess of 140 BHS points. He has also had his share of media acclaim, appearing on Pebble Mill television as a celebrity.

Although Klaus is king, a bay spotted blanket gelding must come a close runner up in the performance stakes and takes precedence in eventing. Merely Diandz (1977), by Pendean Bobby out of Merely a Legend (TB), is big, scopey and talented. Successful in the show ring, he exhibits his talents best in horse trials, where he has frequently galloped and jumped the solid-coloured horses into second place behind him. Amongst victories he counts Wendover and Pebworth Vale. Adept at dressage, too, Merely Diandz and Klaus have teamed up in a joint fund-raising demonstration for charity, their tests being ridden to music with riders attired in eighteenth-century costume after the fashion adopted by the Spanish Riding School.

Klaus and Merely Diandz have led Rivaz performance for close to a decade, but other horses have also shared the limelight. Amongst many were Applejack, who joins the select band of Appaloosas used by whippers-in and huntsmen. In his case he has done double duty in these capacities for the Enfield Chace Hunt. His stable companion Tory followed Petrukas on to the polo field, and The Leopard showed a clean pair of heels over show-jump and event courses. The current mainstay is the bay blanketed Rivaz Vallei, a 16.2 hh gelding by Klaus out of Greta Garbo (TB). He regularly competes in dressage and show jumping, but his forte is team chasing in which he excels.

To the casual observer Klaus overshadows his stablemates, but the Rivaz Stud had many strengths. One was undoubtedly the quality of their mares, and a look at past results of just the National Show alone is very revealing. Over a six-year period from 1977 to 1983, amongst the winners of the in-hand classes for mares and broodmares the names Harmony, Charade, Gaiety Girl, Burletta, Maggie Thatcher, and Duet, all bearing the Rivaz prefix, plus the very early mares Asterisk, Spot On, Tory, Arlecchina and of course Petrukas appear regularly. Many were also good performance mares before retiring to stud.

Applejack, an early Rivaz horse, shown out with the Enfield Chace Hunt.

Rivaz Appaloosas at an Enfield Chace meet at Knebworth House: (*left*) the mare Asterisk and (*right*) stallion Pendean Bobby.

Subsequently the pattern changed, and though the Rivaz Stud continued to produce winners naturally many were the progeny of these mares by the stallions Klaus and Pendean Bobby. Many British breeders' foundation stock stems from the Rivaz Stud, with either outright purchase of progeny or with foals sired by the stallions. The BApS National Champion mare Rodega Keziah is by Klaus, and his sons Rivaz Limerick, also a National Champion, Rivaz Northlight and Rivaz Maestro have helped bring other well-known studs into the Appaloosa business.

It may seem as if Rivaz domination was achieved by pure numerical superiority and the law of averages, and in some measure this was true, but right from the start of the BApS Desmie and Ken de Rivaz insisted on quality, and were leaders in changing the whole concept of the British Appaloosa from its early image, which contained too much ill-bred coarseness with spots, to that of the elegant animals now being seen throughout Britain. Other breeders have done their share, but where it counted most – that first fifteen years – the Appaloosas from the Rivaz Stud made a tremendous difference, the beneficial impact of which will be felt for generations. That, allied with the current trend of importing quality Appaloosas from the USA whose old lines are untampered with by excessive CPO outcrossing influence, augurs well for the British Appaloosa.

On reaching retirement, Ken and Desmie disbanded the stud, their daughter Anne retaining Klaus and a handful of eventing Appaloosas, but their gift to the British breed spreads with each new season's foal crop.

Sutter's Showboat

America's loss was Britain's gain, albeit of too brief a nature, when Sutter's Showboat arrived at Susan McGuinness's Newmarket stables in October 1976.

Somehow in the many stages of his sale and onward shipment to Australia his record as a show jumper was lost and he had contracted a severe wind ailment as a result of poor management. This precluded onward shipment to Australia so Susan was left with a highly coloured horse that raised a few eyebrows when he was ridden through the Mecca of British racing. Once cured by a change of diet a new life started for the stallion when Susan loaned him to Luca Cumani, one of the leading racehorse trainers in Britain. Luca used him as a trainer's hack on Newmarket Heath, and Showboat would stand quietly, unattended, if his rider needed to dismount – a severe test for a stallion with fillies and colts hurtling by on the gallops.

Later Susan began to take him to shows, and in seven outings he racked up eight wins and five seconds in jumping classes. She little realized that he had already had a full career as a champion show jumper in California. When her husband traced the horse's career before export he found that among his credits was State Champion Open Jumper at the 26th Annual California State Horsemen's Association Champion Horse Show in 1970, the largest show ever held in the state, and a continuing list of major show-jumping wins in later years. His sire was Sutter's Showboy, himself an Open Jumper Champion and Pacific Coast Hunter Jumper Association Horse of the Year. Showboat traces back through Bear Paw to Knobby, one of the early Appaloosa sires, foaled in 1918 and therefore before the registry was formed. On his sire's side he has a double cross to Toby I (F.203), one of the most

The sire of Sutter's Showboat was Sutter's Showboy, champion show jumper in the USA in the hands of owner Robert Heilmann, trainer Don Dodge and rider Pancho Frankel.

99

noted foundation sires in the breed's history. The line is rich in jumping horses; even Knobby, an all-round 'using' horse, was a capable jumper well before jumping had become so popular.

In Britain, due to lack of facilities, as it was not originally intended that he should stay let alone stand at stud with the McGuinnesses, Showboat had relatively few mares. He mostly travelled to his wives in old-time fashion. However, from the few direct descendants he sired many have inherited his ability. All have shown colour, and although some are not registered as Appaloosas they carry the blood. He has two representatives standing at stud in Britain: the 16 hand blanket spotted Thundercloud is in the north of England, and Rodega Tobias, a red leopard with a host of awards under saddle and showing early talent over fences, is in East Anglia. Other offspring are the two Appaloosa show jumpers owned by Debbie Plumley and her sister. Monterey and Sandy Toes are full brother and sister out of a Thoroughbred mare, Haunton Charm.

Sadly Showboat's full potential as a stallion was never realized, as he died in 1981 just before the wider national acceptance of the Appaloosa in Britain.

Capitall Stud

Situated in the valley of the River Dee in Clwyd, Capitall Stud is one of the most influential Appaloosa establishments in Britain. Owned by John and Joan Sillitoe it owes its start to mare power.

Chanson Bleu, a tri-coloured leopard mare foaled in 1970, was by an American stallion based in Ireland. The Sillitoes purchased her from Fred Harthill, better known for his international show jumper Penwood Forge Mill. Unfortunately her pedigree did not come with her. In her new ownership she became the foundation mare of Capitall Stud, but not before she had proved herself as an all-round, tough performance mare. She also has the distinction of earning an HIS broodmare premium, an award only going to quality horses of correct hunter conformation.

Chanson Bleu has produced a succession of well-marked foals, all of whom have been big winners in the show ring. In particular she has achieved what is known as a 'good nick' with the HIS Premium stallion Paper Cap (TB), a grandson of Derby Winner Pinza. Of her foals by Paper Cap the two best-known are the mare Capitall Martha and the stallion Capitall Cyril, a tri-coloured leopard standing 15.2 hh and foaled in 1977.

Cyril was really the pivot on which the stud's performance power turned, as he was

Full brother and sister by Paper Cap (TB) out of Chanson Bleu: Capitall Martha (*above*) and Capitall Cyril (*below*), owned and bred by John and Joan Sillitoe.

equally at home in the hunting field and the show ring, achieving success in a wide variety of performance events, including sidesaddle. Sadly he had all too short a life at stud, dying early in 1989 of a clostridium infection from ingesting infected hay in the lambing shed.

His offspring have made an impact on the Appaloosa scene, at the same time being among the first of the breed to be widely accepted in hunter classes – tribute, maybe, to changing reactions from conservative hunter judges, but more to the standards of conformation and ability reached by Capitall horses. Select outcrossing to the Thoroughbred has been used, and in the second generation a very limited amount of line breeding. The Sillitoes are one of the few breeders in Britain who have succeeded in a very short space of time in producing Appaloosas who breed true to type, in this case accepted hunter conformation combined with the distinctive Appaloosa coat patterns. Competing regularly at the major open shows in the West and in County level Appaloosa divisions nationwide, the Capitall horses are hard to beat. They are also much in demand both at home and abroad, and several have been exported to Europe and the Middle East. A major boost to the breed is the position Capitall Harold holds as senior stallion at the Sultan of Oman's Royal Omani stables at Ruwi.

Mares retained by the stud, in addition to Chanson Bleu, are Capitall Martha and Capitall Gladys. The addition of outside blood from the Rivaz stud is via Rivaz Impala by Klaus ex Rivaz Burletta, as well as a small band of select non-Appaloosa stock. Joan Sillitoe says that the proportion of colour to solid horses at Capitall is in the region of 60 per cent colour to 40 per cent solid colour. She states that for Capitall Stud a solid-colour horse with Appaloosa breeding has a high value, as it frequently produces the best coloured horses in the succeeding generation.

It is on the youngster Capitall Hefin, by Capitall Cyril out of Inca Princess, that

Capitall Hefin, by Capitall Cyril out of Inca Princess, winner of the yearling class at the 1989 National Show.

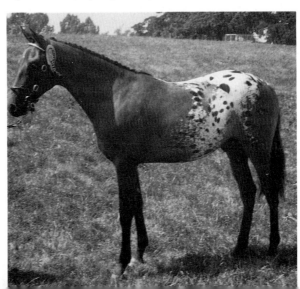

major hopes rest. He is a bay spotted blanket horse that exudes quality. In his yearling season he has had a continuing run of first place awards, being unbeaten in 1989 with eight straight wins. It is through Capitall Luke, full brother to Hefin but sold prior to Cyril's untimely death, that the recent line breeding has been achieved, with foals out of Capitall Martha and Chanson Bleu, the results of which are so good that Capitall Hefin will be used in a similar programme. Capitall Hefin's major success as a yearling in 1989 was winning the yearling class at the National Show, and of any Appaloosa I should have liked to take home Hefin's looks and personality made him my number one choice.

Capitall Harold

After a passage of some twenty-three centuries the Appaloosa has returned close to his historical homeland. With just the narrow Straits of Hormuz separating Oman from Iran (Persia), a twentieth-century Appaloosa stallion is helping to reintroduce the breed to the Middle East.

Capitall Harold (1984), a chestnut with a spotted blanket who stands 14.3 hh, is by Capitall Cyril out of champion mare Sheena. He was presented to Sultan Qaboos bin Said by HRH Prince Charles as a personal gift on his visit to the Sultanate in 1986.

Knowing that one of the Sultan's main interests is horses, Prince Charles was keen to give something of prestige and originality. Captain James Mackie was asked by the Palace what would be most suitable. Captain Mackie had been an officer in the Household Cavalry Regiment, the Blues and Royals, and had subsequently spent several years in the Sultanate of Oman setting up and commanding a cavalry unit for the Sultan, using both purebred Arabian horses and imported troop horses. The Sultan already had a small nucleus of American Appaloosas and Captain Mackie suggested a quality British Appaloosa.

The Capitall Stud horses had proved their worth against the best in Britain with a continuous string of successes at County and National Show level. Capitall Harold had an enviable show record with a fistful of hunter awards, championships and reserve championships, topped by a win in the 1986 Junior Stallion class at the National Show. He was the chosen gift. As he was intended for stud duties in Oman, it was important to have an idea of what type of foals he was likely to throw, and his sire Capitall Cyril had sired multiple winners, including the Female Champion in 1983 and 1985.

To this day the export of horses to the Middle East has received a bad press in

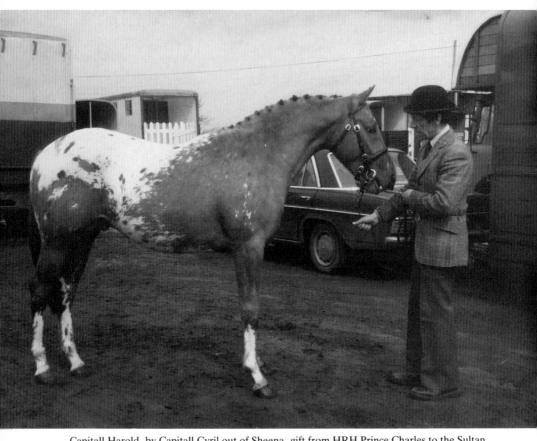

Capitall Harold, by Capitall Cyril out of Sheena, gift from HRH Prince Charles to the Sultan of Oman.

Britain due largely to the atrocious treatment meted out to ex-military horses in Egypt. British Appaloosa enthusiasts can rest easy on Capitall Harold's account. Oman has a wonderful history of horse expertise. The Sultan himself has well-stocked stables with horses for military, civilian and polo use, plus his small Appaloosa herd. These are under the supervision and care of British veterinary surgeons.

On a visit to Oman in 1988 Captain Mackie was able to verify that Capitall Harold was in the best of condition, had settled in well, and is highly esteemed as a first-class stallion.

Tibertich Stud

Where the new American breeds are concerned several studs north of the Border have their priorities right. Manar and Duncrahill specialize in Quarter Horses and Tibertich in Appaloosas. All three put a premium on strong conformation and real performance under stressful conditions.

Nigel and Lucia Boase were first introduced to Appaloosas in Argentina in 1961 and on their return to farm their Lunga Estate at Ardfern in Argyllshire, brought their foundation stock with them: one stallion and two mares, all liver leopards. The prefix Tibertich, a word with Gaelic and Norse overtones appropriately meaning 'Horse Spring', is now found in many other studs, the original Tibertich stallion Chaco having sired progeny that were in demand in Holland as well as England. The Tibertich nucleus grew from the original three to a current herd that fluctuates between twenty-five and thirty. Fifteen of them are used in the string that tests the Appaloosa's famed toughness and versatility by trekking in the Scottish Highlands, competing in long distance rides, being ridden Western, including carrying out cattle work on the estate, and eventing. The others are broodmares and youngstock.

Tibertich is probably the oldest Appaloosa stud in Britain, and is definitely the oldest still operating. Its horses have also had far-reaching effects on the breeding programmes of other newer and smaller studs that have based their own foundation stock on Tibertich Appaloosas.

Stud policy is aimed at producing a quality all-round animal of 15 to 15.2 hh that will fit in with all Ardfern's activities. Horses must be up to carrying a minimum of 15 stone in weight without loss of ability or quality. To this end a careful breeding policy has been adhered to. Where extra refinement has been needed in the past Thoroughbred blood has been used, though the Boases consider concentrations of over 25 per cent undesirable. In the main, Tibertich has aimed at breeding Appaloosa to Appaloosa and in the process, in addition to stallions of their own breeding, they have used Pendean Bobby, Rivaz Limerick and First Draft.

Elsewhere in this book excessive outcrossing and dilution of Appaloosa strains has been discussed as dangerous to the breed, and the Boases consider that intensifying the Appaloosa characteristics and blood is important. Nevertheless in recent years they have been selectively using Quarter Horse blood to infuse qualities they deem

necessary for the specialized area of use in the fast-expanding Western riding sphere that gives Ardfern its unique place in the British Appaloosa world. After the first cross the resulting Quarter Horse/Appaloosa progeny are then crossed back to Appaloosa lines. The stallion used to infuse the extra agility, muscling and weight-carrying power they require is not just any Quarter Horse but Mr Harmon Zero, the 1977 British National Champion imported from the USA by Manar Stud. To date the results have given the Boases exactly what they were seeking, and in addition many of the progeny boast Appaloosa colouring, although there are some solid coloured

(Opposite page)

The Argentinian-bred Tibertich Chaco, by Pedro Mangini out of Parota, ridden in native style by Nigel Boase of the Tibertich Stud, Argyll.

(Below)

Zero Spot, an example of the successful cross of Quarter Horse Mr Harmon Zero on Tibertich mares.

horses as well. Considering the vagaries of producing high Appaloosa colour Nigel Boase looks on its emergence in this generation as a bonus, putting greater value on ability, conformation and temperament.

Although they use occasional and judicious outcrossing, it is largely due to the Boases campaigning for a strict grading-up system to Stud Book status that British Appaloosas are set on the well-marked road to breed status, with clear registration requirements, rather than the diffusion of aims elsewhere apparent.

Distance precludes much show participation by Tibertich horses, but when they do attend it is mostly in the performance events. Lucia Boase shows her Appaloosas' versatility at the yearly National Show where she enters in Western Pleasure, Riding Horse, and Working Hunter classes, always going home with a fistful of awards. However, the endurance riding field is where her Appaloosas shine, and her two best-known performers are Tibertich Dinero and Errin Woodsorrel, noted in the endurance section. The most recent success is Tibertich Sport, who placed high in the British '100 Mile in One Day' Summer Solstice Ride for 1989 over the demanding Ludlow course.

Rodega Appaloosas

One of the smallest Appaloosa studs in Britain, owned by Bob and Ellie Gale of Histon, Cambridgeshire, has arguably had some of the best results in relation to its size. I have been privileged to have been involved with some of the Rodega horses, most notably Keziah, whom I admit having a definite preference for.

There are four horses at Rodega, and three are out of Keetah, a mare by Bantac Kaliff out of Bantac Rosie. Keetah is a red spot leopard, standing 15.2 hh, a heavily built mare who is not the most beautiful to look at, but she has produced very superior progeny. Too often the stallion is credited with more than his share of the resulting foals if they are good, and the mare rarely gets due acclaim. Keetah's three offspring are all by different stallions – Keziah by Klaus; Tobias by Sutter's Showboat; and Ezra by Move Over Nugget – and all are exceptional.

Rodega Keziah (1979) is a few spot leopard mare, and she came to me as a three year old to be schooled. I had three successful years showing her both in Appaloosa classes and, more importantly for breed promotion, in open competition where she did extremely well, being the only Appaloosa to date to win the open Western Pleasure class at the East of England Show, the standard of which is generally higher than anywhere else in the country. At her first attempt she also placed third in the

Rodega Keziah, by Klaus out of Keetah, twice Female Champion at the National Show, ridden by the author.

Stock Horse class at the same show. Keziah always gave her best, and in the ensuing years she has continued to do so back at home, winning an increasing number of awards in performance classes. To her many Western wins she added a fistful of Riding Horse, Working Hunter and dressage triumphs. To accompany these she has an even more impressive array of in-hand trophies, starting at age three with the 1982 huge progeny class at the National Show and a Reserve National Championship Mare award. Ever since these have multiplied. At County shows she frequently wins both in-hand and ridden Appaloosa classes. At the National Show she has gone from strength to strength: 1986, first in the mare class and winner of the progeny award;

Rodega Tobias, by Sutter's Showboat out of Keetah, ridden by Cleo Lewis.

1987, winner of the mare class and the Female Championship; 1988, winner of the mare class, the Female Championship and the progeny award. Ellie says they would love to breed from Kizzy, as she is known, but while she is riding the crest of success it is very hard to take her out of training. To go with her looks and ability she also has an exceptionally kind and willing disposition.

Rodega Tobias (1981) is a red spot leopard 16 hand stallion, who has taken time to come into his own but now seems set to follow in his sister's hoofprints. He is ridden and shown by Bob Gale, who has achieved a similar rapport with him to that I enjoyed with Kizzy. He has not been shown very extensively but he is making his

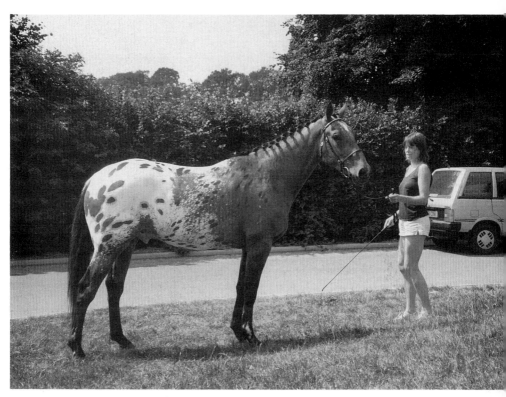

Three-year-old gelding by Rodega Tobias, Chinook owned by E. and L. Randall.

mark in the stallion division. Since 1983, when he was first shown at the National Show, he has worked his way up from a creditable third to take first place in the Senior Stallion class and Reserve Male Champion at the 1988 event. His sire, Sutter's Showboat, the Grade A American Appaloosa show jumper, has passed on his jumping ability and Tobias is showing an aptitude for high flying, adding show jumping and Working Hunter to his other successes. He has already placed above Stephen Smith of the Sanyo stable in one of his earlier jumping trials. His other awards under saddle include placings in both Western Pleasure classes and dressage competitions.

Rodega Ezra, as the youngest of Keetah's trio, is only just starting out but he has already made an impact with a second in the yearling class at the National Show, and did one better at his first show of the 1989 season at Letchworth.

Rodega Stud uses the best stallions available on a mare that must be one of the top producers in the Appaloosa breed in Britain, if judged by the successes of her progeny to date. Another Move Over Nugget foal is eagerly awaited at the time of writing.

Move Over Nugget

A black spotted blanket 15 hand stallion, foaled in 1978 at the Caldwell Ranch in Washington, Oklahoma, Move Over Nugget was imported by Brenda and John George in 1979. I first saw him in 1980 when I judged him in the Appaloosa in-hand class at the Western Horsemen's Association National Championships, and for me there was no contest. Strong believers in the value of a sound pedigree, the Georges brought Move Over Nugget to England because they could not find a horse here that satisfied their requirements. They felt that breeding from a horse with a well-documented, performance-based background lessened the risks of the 'unknown factors' inherent in any breeding programme.

It was a move that proved worthwhile because, although shown very little, he has fulfilled expectations and sired many excellent foals from both Appaloosa and non-Appaloosa mares. Brenda George calculates that he throws 70 per cent colour on mares with no Appaloosa breeding and a higher rate of colour with Appaloosa mares. His progeny are in demand, selling well in England and on the Continent, and all are stamped with his quality and inherit his good temperament. Those of his sons and daughters that have been shown have been top prizewinners.

Apart from the obvious appeal of a well-bred horse with a seven-generation

Move Over Nugget, by Nugget Again, bred at the Caldwell Ranch in Oklahoma and imported to England by Brenda and John George.

pedigree brim full of champions, Move Over Nugget embodies the Georges' ideal of an up-to-weight quality family horse that is a real pleasure to ride.

His sire Nugget Again was a medallion winner in the ApHC's distance riding programme, as well as halter champion in five states, proving that looks and ability are compatible. His grandsire is Nugget Jim, a black spot leopard, winner of forty Grand Champion titles in five states. But it is his paternal granddam's pedigree that gives the really interesting picture. Move Over Nugget has a high percentage of Quarter Horse blood in his pedigree, amounting to 50 per cent if one goes back to the full seven generations. That takes us to well before the days of the Quarter Horse or Appaloosa registries, to when Quarter Horses did not have pedigrees traced with the precision that is necessary today. His granddam Wapitisu was by Wapiti, who was both an Appaloosa and a Quarter Horse, but disbarred from the AQHA registry because of his colour. He was by the stallion Gold Heels (AQHA 1228) out of Cuadroon (AQHA 8588). Wapiti was one of the greats of the Appaloosa breed, the most outstanding sire of halter horses. He was what is known as an AQHA outcrop, a Quarter Horse that shows Appaloosa colour and characteristics. His pedigree goes back to pre-registry days, when some of the horses' bloodlines were either unknown and/or contained high concentrations of non-Quarter Horse blood. In this case Wapiti's parents had crosses to the Roberds horses, in particular the mare Fleet (Flossie) who was a roan Appaloosa mare. His grandsire, Si Ding, a solid colour horse, had a full brother with Appaloosa colouring, Ding Bob II. Coke T. Roberds was known to value a horse for its performance and in his herd he had both Quarter and Appaloosa mares, the latter tracing to his original Appaloosa stallion, a horse with Thoroughbred and Appaloosa parentage known as A-Rab. This goes to show that the specific Appaloosa genes are very prepotent, coming out after several generations of lying dormant. Certain Quarter Horse outcrosses may produce an unexpected bonus for Appaloosa breeders if the pedigree is studied assiduously. The value here is that rather than a dilution of Appaloosa blood a certain percentage of intensification is reached.

Amazing Appaloosas

In the short space of six years Joyce and Jim Nutland have built their Appaloosa stud into a nucleus of horses representative of the best in Britain and America. In addition to running a busy stud Joyce serves on the BApS Committee and campaigned for the introduction of the Stud Book grading-up scheme. Their perfect Appaloosa must

Rivaz Maestro, by Klaus, a Grade D stallion who is one of Joyce and Jim Nutland's Amazing Appaloosas.

have quality combined with performance capabilities and equable temperament, and stud policy was initially aided with the acquisition in 1983 of Rivaz Maestro, who subsequently had a successful career in hand and under saddle.

Using both Rivaz Maestro and his half brother Rivaz Northlight to raise their own first generation mares, their next step was to lease Silver Cloud Kestral. The result is two superb foals – a bay blanket colt and a chestnut blanket filly who are the first Grade B Appaloosas in Britain.

In a search for stock from fresh bloodlines Joyce and Jim toured Appaloosa ranches in the USA, and although they are not advocates of an excessive infusion of Quarter Horse blood, they say that careful outcrossing to quality Quarter Horses has resulted in many superior animals where Appaloosa and Quarter Horse traits complement each other. Recognizing that judiciously used outcrossing is a valuable tool in establishing correct breeding policies, they feel that British Appaloosas can derive benefit from Appaloosas outcrossed with select Quarter Horses, although they readily admit that continuing and excessive dilution of Appaloosa blood, as has happened with the CPO programme current in the USA, is against the breed's best interests. However, with the limited gene pool at present available in Britain outcrossing is still necessary. With the structure of the British Stud Book the safeguard is that outcrossing is only possible at foundation level. This gives double protection – Appaloosa characteristics and blood can be intensified through succeeding generations, and any undesirable tendencies can be eradicated well before Stud Book status is reached.

Their first consignment of American Appaloosas will shortly be putting their stamp on the British scene. Their pride is Amazing Blue (1987), a black stallion with

Amazing Blue, imported from America by Joyce and Jim Nutland and winner of the Junior Stallion class at the National Show in 1989.

spotted white blanket standing 15.3 hh. This colt traces directly to Bright Eyes Brother on his sire's side and Hayes Roman Cloud on his dam's side, and much is expected from introducing him into their select band. At his first British showing Amazing Blue won the Junior Stallion class and was Reserve National Male Champion for 1989. He shows extreme refinement with a beautiful intelligent head, good limbs and well-sprung pasterns, and has just enough muscling as a two year old to indicate that maturity will see him a superbly proportioned, elegant Appaloosa. He should inject a much-needed boost into some of the present British stock.

The Nutlands stress that mare power is probably more important to the British Appaloosa at present than anything else. Accompanying Amazing Blue is Julu's Cloud-Ette, a chestnut roan spotted mare tracing back to Hayes Roman Cloud on the top line. She is out of Absarokee Two Spot who is a granddaughter of Absarokee Sunset, an all-time great performance horse in the hands of trainer Bob Hankla in the 1960s. One of the most influential American Appaloosa stallions, on the distaff side Absarokee Sunset goes back to both Quarter Horse and Appaloosa blood of the 1930s through a mare named Nancy Lee.

The third current American Appaloosa at the stud is Julu's chestnut blanket colt by Mr Chairman, a world champion stallion who combines the best of Appaloosa and Quarter Horse blood through Bright Luster and the Wiescamp Skipper W line.

Mare power is being heightened with further imports still awaited at the time of writing, among them a mare of Prince Plaudit breeding. Prince Plaudit ranks in the top echelon of Appaloosa stallions and is the product of Appaloosa, Quarter Horse and Thoroughbred blood on his sire Red Plaudit's side, with his dam Princess Rita being an Appendix Quarter Horse (Quarter Horse × Thoroughbred). He was bred at the Wiescamp's Colorado ranch.

The Amazing Appaloosa Farm is set on a course that will have a big impact on British Appaloosas in the immediate future, and far-reaching consequences as the blood becomes diffused amongst that currently available in Britain. Where else in Britain can one find such a concentration of the old foundation lines going back to the early days of the Appaloosa resurgence, and the acknowledged modern greats – lines that include not only the best colour producers, but horses strong in performance credits too?

Centaur Equitation Centre

It may not seem a likely place to find some of the best Appaloosas in Britain, but once inside the huge old-fashioned yard, with its adjacent indoor school and undulating acres of cross country fences with a wide variety of solid obstacles, it is possible to see a really representative cross section of the Appaloosa breed. Jim Dobson has more than thirty years' experience breeding, training and riding Appaloosas, and even more as a professional horseman, so he knows a thing or two about quality horseflesh and what makes a good performance horse.

I was fortunate to spend an afternoon at Centaur and Jim took me on a tour of the broodmare band and youngstock herd. As it was pouring with rain the two stallions were put through their paces in the indoor school. There are upwards of thirty registered Appaloosas at Centaur, plus a mini-herd of spotted ponies for children to ride, as well as solid colour horses, but the Appaloosas dominate. This high concentration of talent and colour gives Centaur an absolutely unique place in the English Appaloosa scene, as does Tibertich for Scotland, as literally hundreds of riders are introduced to Appaloosas at the very beginning of their riding careers. However, let no one think this is just an ordinary riding school, for Centaur Appaloosas have exhibited plenty of talent in stressful occupations over the years.

Regular hunting with the Cottesmore and Quorn hunts is a prime activity, in particular with the two stallions First Draft and Rivaz Limerick. Jim reserves First Draft as his personal mount, and Rivaz Limerick has been the mount of Quorn whipper-in, John Seaton, for the past two seasons. As a means of promoting the Appaloosa nothing could be better. Rivaz Limerick, by Klaus out of Rivaz Georgia, is a 16.1 hh chestnut with white blanket that extends to near the withers. Foaled in 1982 he was National Junior Champion at the 1985 National Show and has matured into a superb horse, strong and robust with a very good set of limbs and hooves, sound and very kind. Although Jim does not show extensively, when he does the rest had better beware! Rivaz Limerick made a return trip to the National Show in 1989 and came away with Senior and Overall Male Champion, plus a host of awards under saddle. I had the distinct impression that he would definitely give a super day's hunting, be fresh at the end and take care of his rider into the bargain should emergencies arise. He has a terrific jump in him and is totally honest over even the biggest fence.

Centaur's other stallion is First Draft, a completely different type of horse in colouring and physique, and one with a fascinating history and on his sire's side the most blue-blooded pedigree imaginable.

First Draft is by First Secretary, who was the very first foal of the American Triple Crown winner Secretariat, who had a lifetime's winnings of $1,316,808. With such a

118

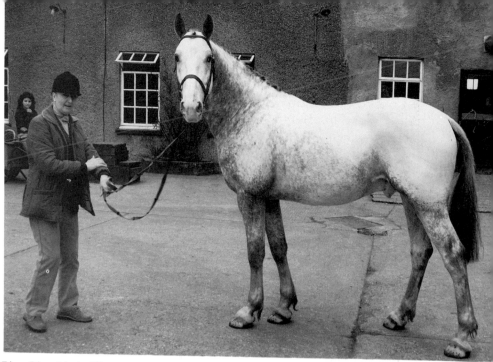

Rivaz Limerick, by Klaus out of Rivaz Georgia, National Junior Champion Stallion in 1985 and Male Champion in 1989, owned by Jim Dobson of the Centaur Equitation Centre.

First Draft, by First Secretary by Secretariat (TB), American-bred Appaloosa stallion owned by the Centaur Equitation Centre.

valuable property it was vital to prove that Secretariat was fertile, especially as the insurers, Lloyds of London, were demanding a definite answer one way or the other. To this end a test mare, who just happened to be an Appaloosa called Leola, was used, and when the tests proved positive the mare had a queue a mile long waiting to buy her. The lucky man was Jack Nankivil of Sahaptin Farm, near Winona, Minnesota. The foal, born in November 1974 with Appaloosa colouring, was named First Secretary and grew to 17 hands, in turn siring foals with good colour and size. His representative in Europe stands over 16.2 hh and is a horse with exceptional quality and refinement. His early blanket with spots has developed to a near leopard colouring on a blue roan base, and he is siring both quality and colour from all types of mares. I was particularly impressed by a bay blanketed colt by First Draft out of a red spot near leopard mare. This foal oozed quality. Much British stock is of rather heavy build and Jim Dobson is fortunate in possessing two such dissimilar stallions so that the heavier stock can be crossed with First Draft, while Limerick is used on mares needing somewhat more substance. In the spring of 1989 when I saw First Draft he had already covered thirty-four mares, was hard and fit, and the equal of Limerick in his ability over some very sizeable fences.

Jim considers First Draft to be arguably the best-bred Appaloosa stallion standing at stud in Europe today. He is more than proving himself as his youngstock are good

Foal by First Draft at the Centaur Equitation Centre.

winners at open shows as well as Appaloosa events. Centaur aims high, showing the youngstock at County level, and awards have been accrued in the Hunter Youngstock classes at Rutland, Royal, Newark and Notts, and Peterborough Shows. At Peterborough an Appaloosa yearling by First Draft won the coveted National Hunter Improvement Society's yearling award. An owner can aim no higher! An indication of his quality is that a French breeder regularly sends stock to be covered by First Draft.

However much the current Centaur stallions fill the eye, it is on other Appaloosas that the centre's early reputation was made, starting with a chance buy about thirty years ago of Jim's foundation stallion The Rock, a 16.2 few spot red leopard which he bought at the famous Appleby Fair in Yorkshire. At first Jim walked away from the transaction with The Rock's 'gipsy' owner over a disagreement of £2.50 in the price. Lured back by the colt's quality he paid the final asking price of £135, and the 'gipsy' gave him a fiver back for luck. When the horse's papers arrived in the post the 'gipsy' turned out to be one of Scotland's richest construction engineers!

Jim said at first there was considerable antipathy towards his stallion on account of his colour, but his performance as a three-day eventer and show jumper soon silenced that. He was the first of many such Appaloosas at Centaur. His son Rockwell was a terrific all round performance horse – a Grade B show jumper, adept at dressage, and successful in national and international eventing. However, his best-known performance Appaloosa in open competition to date has been Trader Joe, a chestnut with spotted blanket, a grandson of The Rock. His forte has been in eventing, and in six outings only he managed to rack up two firsts, two seconds and one third, and competed in dressage at Intermediate level.

Stud policy is to use the best blood available to maintain quality, and some mares are sent to outstanding stallions at other studs. On the matter of outcrossing Jim is positive that only approved stallions should be used, and he admits to a preference for using Thoroughbred blood when such outcrossing is indicated. His observation concerning offspring of Appaloosa matings is that the coloured foals seem to inherit the Appaloosa disposition and characteristics along with boldness and curiosity. Such an observation by one with his experience is well worth serious consideration.

Appaloosas in dressage

Dressage is arguably the most difficult discipline to master if a rider wishes to take his horse to the top. It demands years of intense application and dedication on the rider's part and the partnership and rapport with a horse that is both intelligent and a supreme athlete. Both Britain and America have worthy Appaloosa contenders for dressage honours.

Cockley Cley Weatherman

A strawberry roan 16 hand spotted blanket gelding, foaled in 1977, Cockley Cley Weatherman must surely be the flag bearer for the breed in Britain, as a talented ambassador when competing in international dressage competitions. Eight of his twelve years have been spent at the top level in a variety of events, performing equally well in Appaloosa and open competition. His first two years were under the guidance of Andy Wright and I had the pleasure, when co-judging at the 1982 National Show, of riding him. He went like silk – smooth gaits and sensitive to the very lightest aids.

In 1983 the Willmer family bought him for their daughter Bay-Sarah, affectionately known as Brugs. His role was as a potential Young Riders dressage

Cockley Cley Weatherman and Brugs Nichols, competing in dressage at Grand Prix level.

horse. Weatherman, nicknamed Spotty, had already competed at Medium level but Brugs admits to a rough passage in the first year where the communication lines frequently got crossed. Early dressage entries occasionally resulted in less of the forward movement and rather too much of reverse, as Spotty had a distinct aversion to entering the arena and when he did fought shy of the judge's end, with understandably low marks.

Not an auspicious start!

Brugs admits that it took a whole year to become a team. Even so by the end of the season enough rapport existed for Brugs and Cockley Cley Weatherman to represent Britain at the CDAY (friendly international for young riders) at Goodwood, where they finished a creditable sixteenth from a large entry. The next season was a great improvement, the pair again representing Great Britain in the Young Riders International. The requirements were raised to Prix St George level, and the test suited Weatherman as he was more adept at some elements. Their best year was still to come in 1985. The partnership was maturing and producing some very good results, the best of which was the International CDAY at Goodwood where they were the only British partnership to win a prize.

Always placing well up the entry list, Weatherman gave Brugs four years in the Young Riders dressage arena preparatory to entering the tougher world of open international competition. Wisely, trainer Herr Rochowansky restricted the pair to riding *hors concours* at only one event. However, this gave them the feel of heightened competition at Grand Prix level and during 1988 they earnt 14 grading points in Grand Prix, thus entitling them to compete at the National Dressage Championships at Grand Prix level in September. This event draws riders from all over the world and must be nerve racking for a first time entrant, even when prefaced by Young Rider level preparation. Solid training paid off and a super test ensured team selection to represent Britain in a CDA competition in Holland. As the season closed Brugs felt Weatherman had really excelled himself in his first year at open international level.

He stays fresh in the dressage arena because his life is not restricted, as is that of so many dressage horses, to constant schooling. He enjoys a variety of events – hunting, jumping, earning a fair array of working hunter awards, escorting riders out hacking, and the ham in him enjoys being a celebrity horse opening fairs and fetes, even relishing the odd cup of tea. Between them Cockley Cley Weatherman and Klaus, who now resides with the Willmers, have virtually dominated the over 15 hand Riding Horse class at the National Show, going turn and turn about to stand first –

just occasionally sharing the honours. They were joint honour escorts too at Brugs' wedding in 1988 to Francis Nichols, an instructor in the Household Cavalry.

As an Appaloosa, Weatherman is all that the breed propaganda claims, but maybe Brugs' own words describe it better: 'Weatherman is happy and outgoing and always tries to please; always has his tiny ears pricked forward. He is so intelligent it is untrue. I love him dearly and can't imagine life without him.' As a dressage horse he is still young, the future's strongest challenge being to compete at Senior International level, the first Appaloosa in the world known to do so.

Dickys Chaparral

A 'horse for all reasons', Dickys Chaparral is a black stallion with an extended loud leopard blanket. Foaled in the USA in 1967 he is still going strong at 22, and during his life has carried the Appaloosa flag into many new fields. Early years were spent herding cattle on the Lazy Double Heart Ranch in Acampo, California. There he might have stayed but for a chance visit by Dick and Barbara Reese of American

Dickys Chaparral, successful in the American show ring and dressage arena.

Heritage Warmbloods in Windsor, California, into whose partnership he passed as a four year old.

A highly successful show career followed, dominated by first places and championships at halter, and in English and Western pleasure. However, Barbara Reese knew that, good as these wins were, the stallion's potential was not being realized, and when the chance came for Michael Norreel, a graduate from the famous French Academy at Saumur, to undertake the stallion's dressage training his full talent emerged.

He was one of the first Appaloosas to give dressage demonstrations around his home state and to compete successfully in open competition against established dressage stars at second and third level events. He received loud acclaim for his 1975 exhibition at the Appaloosa Nationals. Concurrently he led a busy life at home as a covering stallion. As such it is all the more remarkable that other facets of his talent came to the fore – talents that need the complete reliability and unflappable docility usually associated with aged geldings. Dickys Chaparral added the distinction of being the only stallion and the first Appaloosa to be registered with the American Vaulting Association, having brought youngsters through to silver medal standard. He also fills number one place in the Sonoma County, California, programme for riding for the disabled. A grateful rider who signs herself simply 'Abby' credits Dickys Chaparral with helping to restore feeling to her lower back and pelvic area which were paralysed in a car crash.

On the flip side of the coin this docile stallion can also ham it up with the best, appearing on the Falcon Crest television series, relishing his share of the adulation that all the stars receive.

Dickys Chaparral has done more for promoting Appaloosas by actually proving the claims for versatility and superb temperament in some of the most difficult and diverse fields imaginable than any amount of 'within breed' competition could achieve.

Appaloosas in endurance riding

The following short list of Appaloosas that have done well in endurance riding is included because this is one aspect in which Appaloosas can excel. There is no judging criteria dependent on arbitrary choice. In America the ApHC has its own distance riding programme. It was largely devised and subsequently put into operation by Sharon Saare, and such was its success in the earlier years of American endurance riding that the American Endurance Ride Conference based their own system upon that of the ApHC. As such the ApHC and its distance riding consultant have had a direct influence on the International Distance Riding programme now operating throughout the world. In America both the distance riding scene and the number of Appaloosas is much larger than in Britain, and consequently Appaloosas have had greater opportunity to record both high mileage and prestigious wins in both Appaloosa and open competition. In Britain, as the sport grows and as the breed's popularity increases it is hoped that other good Appaloosas will join the group of British riders that are proving their breed's toughness on British trails.

American endurance Appaloosas

Although he only competed once, Easter Ute nevertheless holds his position because of the influence he was able to bring to bear during one of the rough patches endurance riding found itself going through in the mid 1960s. Unfounded criticisms of cruelty were being levied against endurance riding, and in particular against the Tevis Cup 100-mile ride, because it held premier position in the sport, by various national humane groups who had not bothered to get their facts right. One such example was the portrayal of a horse stretching to perform the perfectly natural function of urinating as a form of distress! Sharon Saare was at the time involved in the organization of and competing in various endurance events, and saw the way to debunk the charges was to enter a 'name' into the sport.

Actor James Drury of the television series *The Virginian* was at the height of his fame and his favourite mount was an Appaloosa gelding, Easter Ute. Sharon partnered the gelding to a well-deserved completion in the 1967 Tevis Cup Ride, the first 100-miler for both her and Easter Ute. Since then her name has been synonymous with education in the distance riding field in the USA, and in particular with the ApHC's Distance Riding programme.

Many Appaloosas have been prominent in the sport and have kept the breed banner flying. A real trailblazer was Betty Veal's Crow, a leopard marked horse and the first Appaloosa to complete the Tevis Cup ride, who was succeeded by Walter Tibbitts' Ruff Spot's Banner, a blanket marked gelding that became a Tevis Cup ride

(Opposite page)

Easter Ute (*above*), owned by actor James Drury and ridden by Sharon Saare in the 1967 Tevis Cup 100-mile endurance ride; (*below*) Walter Tibbitts and Ruff Spot's Banner competing in the Tevis Cup Ride in 1969.

Antelope New Moon, first Appaloosa to win the NATRC President's Cup, shown with Beverly Tibbitts on an NATRC Competitive Trail Ride.

specialist and multi-buckle winner. The highspot of his career was his award of the Haggin Cup for Best Condition in 1969. In addition he won Regional and National trophies in NATRC, and the Cal-Western Appaloosa Championship for top competitive ride Appaloosa in the state in 1971 and Reserve Champion endurance horse for 1972 and 1973.

Antelope New Moon also came from the Tibbitts' stable. Ridden by Beverly Tibbitts, Annie, as she was stable named, was the first Appaloosa ever to win the NATRC President's Cup awarded annually to the National Sweepstakes Champion Horse on a point system. In the same year (1979), this tough mare also won the NATRC Lightweight Championship, and a fistful of Appaloosa breed awards, finishing the season as Cal-Western Appaloosa State Champion Competitive Trail Horse.

Ring O Fire and Trilby Pederson were one of the toughest partnerships in AERC competitions in the mid 1980s. Trilby only started riding in her forties and owned her first horse at age forty-five. She chose an Appaloosa because of the colour, admits to being more than green, and gives the Appaloosa Ring O Fire full credit for babysitting her through her first four seasons of endurance riding. The Appaloosa gelding has chalked up 3,125 miles of AERC competition in this four-year stint, and in his first full year earned a Tevis Cup Completion award, placed twenty-first in the National AERC rankings amongst literally thousands of horses, won his first Chief Joseph Award, won the California State Appaloosa Endurance Award, and the NATRC National Championship. The following year he won a Double Chief Joseph Award, and continued to repeat his California State Award for three more years in succession. His owner, a glutton for punishment, also attempted to be the highest mileage rider in 1986, being beaten at the post by Les Carr by only 100 miles. Trilby had ridden 7,115 endurance miles in one competitive season.

The last of the American Appaloosas, chosen not necessarily for their wins only but for some unusual aspect of their distance riding careers, is Arab Incognito. 'Nito', as he is nicknamed, is a dun, unregistered half Arabian, half Appaloosa just a shade under 14 hands high. He is owned by Ripley Tate. 'Nito' shows his Appaloosa heritage in a clustering of white spots on his rump, hardly even a blanket, and in his phenomenal endurance abilities.

Initially Linda Tate bought him for her son to ride in pony hunter classes. Nito did well, but it was when they started CTRs that the little Appaloosa/Arab cross showed his mettle, winning right from the start as a four year old in 1982 in novice classes. As he matured he won repeatedly in NATRC open divisions. In his first open year in

1984 he took part in sixteen NATRC rides with many end-of-year awards: National Junior Horse of the Year; National High Point Half-Arabian; Runner up for the President's Cup, and fourth in Grand Championship Division – not bad for a six-year-old pony and twelve-year-old Ripley, who also won prestigious rider awards. By the end of their second open season they had accumulated 1,510 miles and judges were beginning to comment that Ripley at five foot eleven inches, though a flyweight, was too big for the pony.

A change of riders to Linda enabled Nito to continue his winning ways, emerging as 1986 National Grand Champion with the highest average score ever recorded over the season's entries, plus the Half-Arabian award yet again. In 1987 he moved on to AERC events and immediately started winning and placing. In seven rides he had two wins at fifty miles, a second at sixty, a third at fifty, and a second at seventy-five miles.

Because he is just shy of 14 hands it is not possible for Arab Incognito to be registered in the ApHC, in spite of his parentage. The Appaloosa half of his blood never gets the recognition that the half-Arabian side gains, but nevertheless this small powerhouse must be just about the most successful part-Appaloosa in recent years, even though his larger kin gain breed status and breed awards. In open competition he has blazed his own wide trail at complete divergence with his lack of size. As Linda Tate says, 'Nito isn't small. He only takes up a little space.'

British endurance Appaloosas

Fforest Orchid is an Appaloosa mare of unknown breeding and with a totally unknown background when she came into the ownership of Judy Beaumont, who had given her a reprieve from the slaughterhouse, where, alas, even quality horses end up far too often. Things changed rapidly for Orchid as Judy found her to be an exemplary representative of her breed, particularly in the hardiness and endurance aspects.

She has competed in EHPS and BHS endurance rides and in an eight-year span achieved one of the most impressive arrays of endurance trophies ever seen in Britain or Europe. Her major wins include the EHPS of GB Summer Solstice 100-mile ride on two occasions; the 1981 Montcuq 100-mile ride in France; six Gold Awards with the BHS Long Distance Riding Group, plus many other wins at distances ranging from seventy-five to forty miles. There are also countless other placings, usually in the first three, in other endurance rides of fifty miles or more. However, it is not only the individual awards that matter in distance riding, but the cumulative awards that prove the soundness of the contending horses. Orchid proved hers convincingly by twice winning the European Championship in 1980 and 1981: in its early years the rules for this stated that the best three rides would be taken for each horse, one of which, at least, had to be competed for outside the horse's country of domicile. At the end of eight tough years of competition the mare retired sound to broodmare duties, producing three coloured foals to another of Judy Beaumont's endurance prospects.

R Mellow Kinsman is a bay roan stallion with spotted blanket, foaled in 1977 and imported from America as a foal by Judy Beaumont. He is one of the few Appaloosas in Britain to have achieved a Golden Horseshoe in the prestigious endurance event run over Exmoor's tough terrain, as well as achieving a 100-mile ride completion in a very short endurance career. His talents were in demand in other equestrian fields and he has also won awards for dressage and combined driving events. On the lighter side, he has given driving displays and has been hunted regularly, showing two of the other Appaloosa attributes – versatility coupled with ideal temperament, the latter often tested to the utmost in the hunt field, where some riders are not as careful as they should be when bringing mares alongside.

Tibertich Dinero is by Chaco ex Tibertich Silva. He is a leopard Appaloosa bred by the Boases at Ardfern and is well known in Appaloosa showing circles, being equally talented in Western Pleasure, Riding Horse and Working Hunter events. But his real forte is endurance riding. He has competed successfully and regularly in the events run by the HLDRC, but his highest accolade to date must be as the outright winner of the Best Conditioned horse in the 1987 International Windsor to Paris endurance race of over 250 miles. He was one of the four-strong Scottish team. Ridden by Lucia Boase in a cumulative stress race that took heavy toll of the riders and horses over the eight days, he was one of twenty-one horses out of the initial entry of sixty-four that completed the ride. He was accompanied on this ride by Alison Craig's Appaloosa Tibertich Sport, who was bred at Ardfern. Sport was also one of the few finishers on this memorable ride, but his claim to Appaloosa fame was his placing in the first ten at the Summer Solstice 100-mile ride run by the EHPS of GB in 1989. That year it was run over just about the most demanding course yet, set in the hilly country around Ludlow in one of the hottest, driest summers on British record. In this event, and in particular under these conditions, the Appaloosa toughness was truly tested, especially the hooves, as the going during the summer was iron hard, causing many horses to withdraw or be eliminated from many endurance events.

Tibertich Dinero, by Tibertich Chaco out of Tibertich Silva, pictured with Lucia Boase who has competed successfully on him in a number of endurance rides.

Errin Woodsorrel is an Appaloosa gelding bred by BApS Secretaries Michael and Ann Howkins and owned by Lucia Boase. He is an up-and-coming distance horse and in his first season in 1989 only showed a fragment of a potentially super career, qualifying for the Golden Horseshoe in a forty-mile ride at speeds in excess of 7½ mph, and earning himself a Silver Award at the final 100-mile ride, which is split over two days. Not pushed in his first attempt he came through without a veterinary penalty over the entire two days, and Lucia only missed Gold time by five minutes. Not bad for a young horse over Exmoor's forbidding stretches.

It is to be hoped that as the Appaloosa gains favour in Britain and the sport of distance riding in both Endurance and Competitive Trail divisions grows that the two can come together with more riders campaigning their Appaloosas on the distance trail, and more endurance riders searching for just the right horse to be encouraged to 'Go Appaloosa'. It is not a shot in the dark, an unknown quantity. There has been ample proof in America that the Appaloosa, given the chance, can put his rider in the winning slot, whatever the distance.

Breed promotion through involvement

Although I have briefly mentioned Sharon Saare as Easter Ute's Tevis Cup rider, I feel that here is one person who has added much to the success of the current Appaloosa breed and should be recognized along with the earlier breed promoters.

Sharon's Appaloosa involvement goes back to her teenage days, but her first Appaloosa of popular note was the stallion Leopard Cortez, which she showed successfully and then sold to film star Ben Johnson. Cortez subsequently made quite a name for himself on the big and small screens. After college, Sharon's Appaloosa interests expanded into a fully fledged breeding programme in the early 1960s. She

Actor Ben Johnson riding Patchy.

and her husband Bill also ran a hectic horse trading business, which catered largely to the mushrooming pleasure and show horse industry in California, and involved over 8,500 horses in six years. Their prime requisites in both breeding and selling Appaloosas, as well as other breeds, were soundness and good disposition, and particularly in the Appaloosa breeding operation the conformation needed by an equine athlete: well-defined withers, good feet, and shoulders and back designed to offer a secure saddle position. Sharon deplores the trend in some Appaloosa breeding where the sound serviceability and athleticism of the earlier Appaloosas is being sacrificed for the false values of the current halter show arena.

It was with structurally sound Appaloosas that great strides were made. With Olema Ed, who died in his twenties and whom she describes as a 'mellow and courageous companion', she made the film 'An Introduction to Endurance Riding' that piloted Competitive Trail and Endurance Riding to much of its national acceptance in the USA. Put out by the ApHC in 1971 when Sharon was the driving

Olema Ed pictured during the making of the film 'An Introduction to Endurance Riding'. This film advanced the sport of endurance riding in the USA, as potential competitors could see exactly how a ride operated and what a rider did to complete the course.

force and director of the Club's Distance Riding Programme, the film has had tremendous educational influence on the sport. Olema Ed was a true trail horse campaigner, standing high in the Cal-Western Appaloosa ratings in both Competitive Trail and Endurance categories.

Many American breeders looked to her Elk Grove Ranch for foundation stock, and she made regular trips to Nez Percé country in Idaho and Montana where the beneficial influence of the earlier US Remount Breeding Programmes were still evident in the stock. However, Sharon's influence in Appaloosa breeding did not stop short in California but was to have major international repercussions.

Her senior stallion was Little Bull, by the famous Joker B. Little Bull had inherited both disposition and ability from Joker B and carried Sharon to multiple wins in the show ring as well as performing duty as top wrangle horse and herd sire on the ranch. Clover Joker Bull was by Little Bull out of her mare Ballerina K, and when exported to Australia made a name for himself as a sire and performance horse in the earliest days of Australian Appaloosas, being the first of note to land in the Antipodes. Two other outstanding show performers by Little Bull, bred by Sharon, were Jubullan K and Joker's Velvetine.

Sutter's Showboy earned his earliest recognition as a jumper at Sharon's Elk Grove Ranch. An unusually bred horse, being Appaloosa cross Saddlebred, he was found by Sharon in a dealer's yard in Washington State as a yearling. He soon

Sutter's Showboy competing at the Indio National Horse Show in California, ridden by Pancho Frankel.

Sharon Saare pictured outside the Capitol building in Washington DC with Senator James McClure (centre) and Richard Stanger with the Appaloosa Robaleed Comanche Sheik.

showed his phenomenal athleticism when penned with other young colts by soaring out of the ranch loading chute, clear across the driveway, jumping into show-jumping history. Sharon sold him to Californian Bob Heilmann, who put him in training. In the capable hands of trainer Don Dodge and rider Pancho Frankel he left his mark in America with successes at major California shows such as Monterey, Santa Barbara, Santa Rosa, Indio and Del Mar. The successes continued with his most famous son Sutter's Showboat, and through his grandsons and daughters currently jumping in international and Appaloosa circles in Great Britain.

Many areas of Britain are diabolical for riders, devoid of bridleways and with no provision made by the majority of councils for an expanding pleasure culture based on horse riding. America too has its share of these problems but not to the same degree. The US Congress is reasonably enlightened about land conservation and recognizes individuals' rights to use their natural heritage in the form of National Trails. However, this does not happen by itself. The ApHC run the annual Chief Joseph Trail Ride and it was following Sharon's report to Congress in 1976 that 1,350 miles of the Nez Percé Trail from Wallowa Lake, Oregon, to Idaho were preserved for all time as an historic trail, proof against 'concrete jungle development'. It was Sharon who initiated the idea of preserving the route of the Nez Percé retreat as a National Trail and provided initial testimony to the US Congress, thus achieving 'national designation' which is in process even as this book is being written.

It is to such people as the USA's Sharon Saare and Britain's de Rivaz family, amongst others, that the Appaloosa owes much, and not only the Appaloosa; in many respects using the Appaloosa as a catalyst other riders and their horses also reap a benefit.

Mr and Mrs John Sillitoe's stallion Capitall Cyril with canine friend Mr Wilks.

Bibliography

AERC Yearbook, 1985, 1986

Arlandson, Lee. *Know the Appaloosa Horse.* Farnham Horse Library, 1976

British Appaloosa Society. *Newsletters*, complete, 1976–89

Capon, Edmund. *Art and Archaeology in China.* Macmillan, 1977

Edge, David, and Paddock, John Miles. *Arms and Armour of the Mediaeval Knight.* Defoe, 1988

Firdausi, *Shahnama.* Trans. A. G. and E. Warner (1905–15)

Haddle, Jan. *The Complete Book of the Appaloosa.* A. S. Barnes, 1975

Haines, Francis. *Appaloosa: The Spotted Horse in Art and History.* University of Texas Press, 1963

Hartley Edwards, Capt. E. 'Appaloosa: the do-it-yourself breed', *Riding Magazine*, November 1969

Herodotus. *The Histories.* Trans. Aubrey de Selincourt. Penguin, 1976

Homer. *The Iliad.* Penguin Classics, 1986

Hyland, Ann. *The Endurance Horse.* J. A. Allen, 1988

Hyland, Ann. *Equus: The Horse in Roman Times.* Batsford, 1990

Knabstrup News. Denmark

Loch, Sylvia. *The Royal Horse of Europe.* J. A. Allen, 1986

'Loss for Col. V. D. S. Williams', *Horse and Hound*, 6 August 1971

Ministère de la Culture. *L'Art des Cavernes: Atlas des Grottes Ornées Paléolithiques Françaises.* Ministry of Culture, Paris, 1984

Olivova, Vera. *Sport and Games in the Ancient World.* Guild Publishing, 1984

Oppian. *Cynegetica.* Trans. A. W. Mair. Heinemann, 1928

Prodan, Mario. *An Introduction to Chinese Art.* Hutchinson, 1966

Richardson, Bill and Donna. *The Appaloosa.* Arco, 1977

Robinson, B. W. *Persian Paintings in the John Rylands Library.* Sotheby Parke Bernet, 1980

Saare, Sharon. *Endurance Riding and Management.* ApHC, 1972

Sophocles. *The Electra.* Trans. R. F. Watling. Penguin, 1953

Western Horseman Magazine. Various issues, in particular article on Claude Thompson by Juli Thorson, December 1987

Williams, Dorian. *The Classical Riding Master: The Wilton House Collection.* Eyre Methuen, 1979

Wolfram of Eschenbach. *Willehalm.* Trans. Charles E. Passage. Frederick Unger, 1977

Wright, Margaret. 'The spotted horse's future in Britain', *The Field*, 26 March 1970, pp. 543–4

Abbreviations

AAA	Australian Appaloosa Association, Ltd
AERC	American Endurance Ride Conference
AHS	Arab Horse Society
AHCR	Arabian Horse Club Registry of America
ApHC	Appaloosa Horse Club, Inc.
ApHCC	Appaloosa Horse Club of Canada
AQHA	American Quarter Horse Association
BApS	British Appaloosa Society
BHS	British Horse Society
BSJA	British Show Jumping Association
CDA	Concours Dressage Amité
CDAY	Concours Dressage Amité – Young Riders
CTR	Competitive Trail Ride
EFA	Equestrian Federation of Australia
EFI	Equestrian Federation International
EHPS of GB	Endurance Horse and Pony Society of Great Britain
ER	Endurance Ride
FH	Foundation horse of a breed before a registry was formed
HIS	Hunter Improvement Society
HLDRC	Highland Long Distance Riding Club
HSAA	Horse Shows Association of Australia
KN	Knabstrupperforeninge (Danish Knabstrup Registry)
MAFF	Ministry of Agriculture, Fisheries and Food
NATRC	North American Trail Ride Conference
ROM	Register of Merit
TB	Thoroughbred

Index of horses' names